TRAVEL CAREER DEVELOPMENT

Student Workbook

9th Edition

Patricia J. Gagnon, CTC
Marty Sarbey de Souto, CTC

Table of Contents

Preface

The *Travel Career Development Student Workbook* provides exercises that correspond to each chapter in the *Travel Career Development* textbook. The exercises are designed to reinforce the information you need to know in order to achieve the chapter objectives, to give you a good idea of your understanding of the chapter, and to enhance your understanding of the textbook by having you do further thinking and research.

What Is in the Workbook

The worksheets in Part 1 of the workbook offer many types of exercises. For example, there are exercises that call on you to

- define key terms.
- search the Internet.
- apply or develop your knowledge of geography.
- recall airline and airport codes.
- read schedules.
- analyze tour brochures.
- compare travel products.
- develop critical analysis skills.
- solve problems.
- apply what you have learned to possible situations.
- evaluate your own interests and skills.

Part 2 of the workbook provides sample resources prevalent in the industry. This gives you experience using a typical timetable and itinerary to help you become proficient in working with such standard resources relied on by all segments of the travel/tourism industry. Your instructor may augment these resources by choosing from the many thousands used by industry practitioners today.

How to Study *Travel Career Development*

A good approach to studying *Travel Career Development* is to concentrate on the text first. If your instructor assigns a chapter of the text and the corresponding chapter in the workbook, you may be tempted to first make sure you "get your homework done," going directly to the workbook and trying to answer the questions. We suggest you first concentrate on mastering the chapter:

- Look at the chapter outline and objectives first.
- Preview the chapter, skimming the pages and noticing the major headings. Ask yourself if you know anything about these topics already.
- Read over the key terms at the end of the chapter. Which ones do you know something about? Which ones are new?
- As you read through the chapter, highlight key points or those you might have questions about.
- Stop periodically to check that you have understood and can recall what you've read; doing so helps learning. Instead of reading straight through a chapter, stop after every major head and quiz yourself. The Check-Ups in the textbook help you do that. Although they're not intended to summarize an entire section, they review some key points. Try completing each item yourself after you read the introductory statement. If you can't, go back over the section. You might also use the Check-Ups to help you review for tests.
- Try reading just the first part of the On the Spot boxes; hide the second part of the box with a card or your hand. See how you would deal with the scenario described before going on to read the second part of

the box. (Don't be discouraged, though. Some of the boxes present issues not addressed in the text of the chapter.)

- If you see a term in **_boldface italic_,** it's an important word, one that you should remember and be able to define. You can find definitions not only in the chapter where the term is printed in bold italic but also in the textbook's Glossary. Other important terms are printed in italics.
- Don't forget the Chapter Highlights in the Chapter Wrap-Up. They should help you consolidate your mastery of the chapter and check your understanding, as well as review for tests.

Now you are ready to tackle the exercises in the *Travel Career Development Student Workbook*. The first worksheet in each chapter asks that you define the new terms in that chapter of the textbook. You don't need to give technical definitions. Put the definitions into your own words or the words you might use with clients. Going over these terms is one of the best ways to do a crash review before a test.

Some exercises in the workbook ask that you use outside sources such as newspaper ads, phone conversations with suppliers, or interviews. Look ahead to see which of these exercises you can plan time for. Not all exercises will be done by all classes—some require major course projects. Your instructor will guide you.

One worksheet in each chapter involves the Internet. The goals of these worksheets are to make sure that you are comfortable using the Internet and that you become familiar with the information on major travel/tourism Web sites. These goals are much more important than finding the correct answer to a particular question, because answers may change month to month and sometimes day to day. Furthermore, some sites may change their addresses, and others may cease to function or to be current.

Be flexible in finding information. If the problems working with one Web site seem to be insurmountable, see if you can find another site with the same information. Don't be bogged down on one question, however; it may be better to go on to another and find out the next day if your fellow classmates experienced the same problem.

As you complete these worksheets on the use of technology, make your own lists of favorite Web sites that you might want to use in the future. Also, as you work on the other worksheets, you might want to write the answers on a separate sheet of paper. In that way you can use the workbook (without having the answers staring you in the face) to test yourself before taking classroom quizzes, finals, the Travel Career Development Test, or the National TAP Test.

The last worksheet in each chapter is entitled "Critical Thinking." It is designed to allow you to exercise your ability to examine various topics relevant to the travel industry by gathering information on the subject and offering your own opinions or predictions.

Good luck in using this workbook to learn the course objectives and to reach your personal goals in the travel/tourism industry.

Part 1:
Worksheets

Name _____   Date _____

Directions: Define the following terms.

1. ASTA _____

    _____

2. Benefit _____

    _____

3. Business travel _____

    _____

4. Commission _____

    _____

5. Commodity _____

    _____

6. Conference system _____

    _____

7. Corporate travel _____

    _____

8. Demographic segmentation _____

    _____

9. Dependables _____

    _____

10. Distributor _____

    _____

11. Feature _____

    _____

12. High season _____

    _____

(continued)

13. Hospitality industry _____

_____

14. Incentive travel _____

_____

15. Leisure travel _____

_____

16. Low season _____

_____

17. Marketing _____

_____

18. Market segmentation _____

_____

19. Meeting travel _____

_____

20. NTO _____

_____

21. Online travel agency _____

_____

22. Override _____

_____

23. Personal selling _____

_____

24. Preferred supplier relationship _____

_____

25. Price segmentation _____

_____

(continued)

Name _____   Date _____

26. Professional _____

_____

27. Psychographic segmentation _____

_____

28. Selling _____

_____

29. Shoulder season _____

_____

30. Special-interest travel _____

_____

31. Supplier _____

_____

32. Supporting businesses and organizations _____

_____

33. Target market _____

_____

34. Travel agency _____

_____

35. Travel counselor _____

_____

36. TIA _____

_____

37. Usage segmentation _____

_____

38. VFR travel _____

_____

(continued)

39. Venturers _____

_____

Name _____ Date _____

Directions: Check the Sunday travel section of your newspaper or the newspaper of a major city near you. Choose two advertisements and compare them by answering the following questions:

1. Who is the distributor?

   a. Ad #1 _____

   b. Ad #2 _____

2. What types of suppliers does the ad represent?

   a. Ad #1 _____

   _____

   b. Ad #2 _____

   _____

3. What type(s) of consumer does the ad target?

   a. Ad #1 _____

   _____

   b. Ad #2 _____

   _____

4. Do you think that the ad is effective? Why or why not?

   a. Ad #1 _____

   _____

   _____

   b. Ad #2 _____

   _____

   _____

Name   Date

Directions: Each destination offers a combination of characteristics that makes it unique. Choose a destination with which you are familiar.

Destination: _____

What psychographic segment(s) is likely to be attracted to your destination? (Look again at Figure 1.3 on page 14 in the textbook.) Why?

_____

_____

_____

_____

_____

_____

_____

_____

_____

_____

_____

_____

_____

_____

_____

_____

_____

_____

_____

_____

_____

_____

Name _____   Date _____

Directions: Describe five skill areas needed for entry-level positions in the travel industry and why each is important.

1. Skill area: _____

   _____

   _____

2. Skill area: _____

   _____

   _____

3. Skill area: _____

   _____

   _____

4. Skill area: _____

   _____

   _____

5. Skill area: _____

   _____

   _____

Directions: List five tasks that you have performed in the past two years, and then list the skill area that each falls into. (You may want to refer to this information when you are preparing your résumé.)

6. **Task performed**   **Skill area**

   a. _____   _____

   b. _____   _____

   c. _____   _____

   d. _____   _____

   e. _____   _____

Name _____   Date _____

Directions: Match the mode of travel with the description: (a) air travel, (b) automobile travel, (c) rail transportation, or (d) ship transportation.

1. The major method of travel between continents before the twentieth century

   _____

2. The major method of transcontinental travel in North America a century ago

   _____

3. The type of travel that grew steadily more important throughout the twentieth century, becoming the mode of transportation used for most trips in the United States

   _____

4. The mode of transportation that grew steadily after World War II, influencing every aspect of the travel industry

   _____

Directions: Answer the following questions.

5. What two specific destinations would you recommend to the following types of travelers? Why?

   a. Venturer _____

   _____

   _____

   b. Centric _____

   _____

   _____

   c. Dependable _____

   _____

   _____

6. List and describe four ways to segment markets.

   a. _____

   _____

   b. _____

   _____

(continued)

c. _____

_____

d. _____

_____

7. List three main types of travel and give an example of each.

a. _____

_____

b. _____

_____

c. _____

_____

8. Explain the difference between a feature and a benefit.

_____

_____

_____

_____

Name _____   Date _____

Directions: For practice in using the Web sites of some prominent sources of information on travel and the travel industry, complete the following exercises. (You may wish to add the Web sites mentioned in the Technology Technique worksheets to your list of "favorites" or "bookmarks" for future use.)

1. Go to *Travel Weekly*'s Web site (www.travelweekly.com) on two days. Choose one article that interests you on each day. For each article, write the title and a sentence that explains why it interests you.

   Article #1 _____

   _____

   _____

   Article #2 _____

   _____

   _____

2. Enter a travel-related topic in the Search box at *Travel Weekly*'s site. How many articles related to your topic are listed? Choose one and read it. Write its title, and summarize the article in a paragraph.

   Number of articles _____

   Title and summary of selected article _____

   _____

   _____

   _____

   _____

   _____

   _____

3. Go to the Web site of the U.S. Travel Association (www.ustravel.org), and choose one of its top stories. Write the topic of that story and one sentence explaining why it is important in today's travel climate.

   _____

   _____

   _____

   _____

   _____

(continued)

4. Find and go to the Web site of either the Tourism Industries Office of the International Trade Administration at the U.S. Department of Commerce or the Bureau of Transportation Statistics of the U.S. Department of Transportation. Choose one statistic that might be valuable to you in selling travel, and write one sentence explaining why knowing this statistic might be useful.

Statistic _____

_____

_____

_____

_____

Usefulness _____

_____

_____

_____

_____

5. Go to ASTA's Web site (www.astanet.com). Who is the ASTA agent nearest you? (Tip: Enter your home zip code under "Find an agent.")

_____

Name _____   Date _____

Directions: Consider the following issues. Conduct research to help you respond, and be prepared to discuss the topic in class.

1. Check the Web sites of at least two travel and tourism organizations, and find out their forecasts for the future of the travel industry. What are their projections for the growth of the industry? Do they identify any specific challenges and opportunities?

   _____

   _____

   _____

   _____

   _____

   _____

   _____

   _____

   _____

   _____

2. Many factors have a direct impact on the travel industry. How can changes in economic or political conditions affect a destination's tourism industry? What other factors would have a direct impact on the travel and tourism industry at a destination?

   _____

   _____

   _____

   _____

   _____

   _____

   _____

   _____

   _____

   _____

Name   Date

Directions: Define the following terms.

1. 24-hour clock _____

_____

2. Altitude _____

_____

3. Atlas _____

_____

4. Climate _____

_____

5. Consulate _____

_____

6. Continent _____

_____

7. Destination _____

_____

8. Destination geography _____

_____

9. Destination management and promotion _____

_____

10. Duty _____

_____

11. Duty-free port _____

_____

12. Embassy _____

_____

(continued)

13. Equator _____

_____

14. Exchange rate _____

_____

15. Familiarization trip (fam trip) _____

_____

16. Geography _____

_____

17. GMT _____

_____

18. Gulf _____

_____

19. International date line _____

_____

20. Island _____

_____

21. Isthmus _____

_____

22. Latitude _____

_____

23. Leeward _____

_____

24. Longitude _____

_____

25. Mediterranean climate _____

_____

(continued)

Name _____ Date _____

26. Metric system _____
_____

27. Monsoon _____
_____

28. NTO _____
_____

29. Ocean _____
_____

30. Passport _____
_____

31. Peninsula _____
_____

32. Prime meridian _____
_____

33. River _____
_____

34. Sea _____
_____

35. Sound _____
_____

36. Strait _____
_____

37. Tourist card _____
_____

38. The Travel Institute _____
_____

(continued)

39. UTC _____

_____

40. VAT _____

_____

41. Visa _____

_____

42. Windward _____

_____

Name _____

Date _____

Directions: Each destination offers a combination of characteristics that makes it unique. Choose a destination with which you are familiar.

Destination _____

1. Describe the following characteristics of your destination, and explain how each adds to (or subtracts from) its popularity.

    a. Climate _____

    _____

    _____

    b. Attractions _____

    _____

    _____

    c. Costs and standard of living _____

    _____

    _____

    d. Accessibility_____

    _____

    _____

    e. Culture _____

    _____

    _____

    f. Competition _____

    _____

    _____

2. What other factors make your chosen destination unique?

    _____

    _____

    _____

(continued)

3. Has the appeal of your destination ever changed because of unique circumstances? Explain.

_____

_____

_____

_____

_____

4. Describe travelers who are especially likely to be attracted to your destination. In particular, can you identify demographic and psychographic segments (as discussed in Chapter 1) that are most likely to find the destination appealing? What types of special-interest travel could it attract?

_____

_____

_____

_____

_____

Name _____ Date _____

Directions: Choose the tourist offices of two U.S. states or the NTOs of two international countries. Call each tourist office, request tourist literature, and then answer the following questions.

State or country #1 _____

State or country #2 _____

1. How would you evaluate the customer-service skills of the office?

State or country #1 _____

_____

State or country #2 _____

_____

2. How long did it take to receive the literature?

State or country #1 _____

State or country #2 _____

3. How would you rate the quality of the literature?

State or country #1: _____

_____

State or country #2: _____

_____

4. If clients wanted to visit the state or country, what five attractions would you recommend?

State or country #1 _____

_____

_____

_____

State or country #2 _____

_____

_____

_____

(continued)

5. Did the literature change your perception of the state or country? If so, how?

State or country #1 _____

_____

State or country #2 _____

_____

Name _____ Date _____

Directions: Provide the requested information.

1. List three acceptable proofs of U.S. citizenship.

   a. _____

   b. _____

   c. _____

2. Identify four items that must accompany a completed passport application form.

   a. _____

   b. _____

   c. _____

   d. _____

3. List four types of visas.

   a. _____

   b. _____

   c. _____

   d. _____

4. What document(s) do U.S. citizens need to enter Mexico?

   _____

5. What document(s) do U.S. citizens need to enter Hawaii?

   _____

6. What document(s) do U.S. citizens need to enter China?

   _____

7. What document(s) do U.S. citizens need to enter the United Kingdom?

   _____

8. What document(s) do U.S. citizens need to enter the Bahamas?

   _____

(continued)

Directions: For each scenario, indicate the maximum worth of goods that U.S. residents would be allowed to bring with them back into the country:

9. A family of four (two children, ages 3 and 12) returning from Europe

                  _____

10. A couple returning from Mexico

                  _____

11. A couple returning from the Bahamas

                  _____

12. A couple returning from Canada

                  _____

13. A single person returning from St. Thomas

                  _____

Name   Date

Directions: Circle the letter indicating the best answer to each question.

1. Buying a liter of Burgundy wine in France is the approximate equivalent of buying how much wine in the United States?
   a. A half-pint
   b. A quart
   c. A half-gallon
   d. A gallon

2. Driving the hundred or so kilometers from Madrid to Ávila in Spain is roughly equivalent to driving how many miles in the United States?
   a. 60 miles
   b. 100 miles
   c. 160 miles
   d. 212 miles

3. What kind of U.S. race is roughly equivalent to the 1,500-meter race in Athens?
   a. A 100-yard dash
   b. A one-mile race
   c. A two-mile race
   d. A marathon

4. Buying a kilogram of pasta in Palermo is roughly equivalent to buying how much in the United States?
   a. A quarter-pound
   b. A half-pound
   c. A pound
   d. Two pounds

Directions: Convert the following metric measurements to the system usually used in the United States.

5. 40 liters of petrol (gasoline) in England = _____ U.S. gallons

6. 100 grams of prosciutto in Italy = _____ ounces

7. 550 kilometers on the German autobahn = _____ miles

8. 32° Fahrenheit in Moscow, Idaho = _____ ° Celsius in Moscow, Russia

9. A sign announcing "Zona escuela 40 meters" in Mexico means that the school zone is about how many mile(s) ahead?

(continued)

Directions: Answer the following questions.

10. What recommendations would you give clients traveling abroad who ask advice about using credit cards such as American Express, Diners Club, Visa, or MasterCard?

_____

_____

_____

_____

_____

_____

11. Would you recommend that your clients buy traveler's checks for their vacations? Why or why not?

_____

_____

_____

_____

_____

_____

Name   Date

Directions: Indicate which type of geography is reflected in each of the following statements: locational geography, physical geography, or cultural geography. (Bonus: Name the places described.)

1. Broad rivers flow from the Andes to the Atlantic across this country.

   _____

2. This physically rugged country has Pakistan on its southeastern border and Iran on its western border.

   _____

3. The practice of Hinduism is located primarily on one island of this mostly Islamic archipelago.

   _____

4. An active volcanic landscape, deep valleys, and a mountain rising from the sea to 13,000 feet characterize this U.S. island.

   _____

Directions: Circle the letter indicating the best answer to each question.

5. You can snow-ski in Hawaii primarily because of what characteristic on one island?
   a. Its latitude
   b. Its longitude
   c. Its altitude
   d. The leeward side

6. Which attribute of a location tells you the least about its climate?
   a. Latitude
   b. Longitude
   c. Altitude
   d. Proximity to water

7. Which of these topics should you be most inclined to discuss with your client?
   a. What the weather will be like on the trip
   b. What the climate is like at the destination

8. The prime meridian is also called
   a. the equator.
   b. the Greenwich mean line.
   c. the international date line.
   d. 180° north or south.

(continued)

9. A duty-free port means that
   a. items bought are not taxed but must be used solely for that port.
   b. items bought are not taxed coming into the port but are taxed going out.
   c. items bought are not taxed coming into or out of the port but may be taxed when brought into another country.
   d. items bought are not taxed coming into or out of the port, nor can they be taxed when entering another country.

Directions: Answer the following questions. (Consult an atlas for help.)

10. What two continents are attached to each other by an isthmus that also separates the world's two largest oceans?

11. What two continents meet at a rather small land bridge that also separates two of the world's most important seas?

12. Russia and Turkey are said by most geographers to be the only countries that have part of their land on two continents. What are these two continents?

13. The Western Hemisphere consists of which two continents?

14. Only scientists and visitors (all of whom eventually go home) live on this continent.

15. Flying from Seattle to Honolulu takes you over this ocean.

16. Flying from Australia to Africa takes you over this ocean.

Directions: Indicate whether the following statements are true or false. If a statement is false, rewrite it to create a true statement.

17. A peninsula is a narrow body of land joining two larger bodies of land. True or false?

18. A legend, or key, on a map explains the symbols that are used on the map. True or false?

(continued)

Name   Date

19. The higher the altitude, the warmer the climate is likely to be. True or false?

_____

20. The Gulf Stream is a major warm ocean current that flows north from the Caribbean area. True or false?

_____

21. Longitudes are distances measured north or south of the equator. True or false?

_____

22. Areas with a Mediterranean climate have warm, dry summers and mild, wet winters. True or false?

_____

Directions: Convert the following times from the 24-hour clock to A.M./P.M. format.

23. 1359 _____   25. 0600 _____

24. 2100 _____   26. 1502 _____

Directions: Convert the following to times on the 24-hour clock.

27. 3:25 P.M. _____   29. 8:58 P.M. _____

28. 11:50 A.M. _____   30. 10:05 P.M. _____

Directions: Answer the following questions.

31. If it is 0700 in Chicago, Illinois (GMT -6), what time is it in Honolulu, Hawaii (GMT -10)? Give the answer both according to the 24-hour clock and in A.M./P.M. format.

_____

32. If it is 1400 in Rome, Italy (GMT +1), what time is it in Los Angeles, California (GMT -8)? Give the answer both according to the 24-hour clock and in A.M./P.M. format.

_____

33. If a flight departs London at 1400 (GMT) and arrives in Chicago at 1600 (GMT -6), how long is the flight?

_____

34. If a flight departs Los Angeles at 1600 (GMT -8) and arrives in London at 1000 (GMT) the next day, how long is the flight?

_____

(continued)

35. A direct flight from California to Australia takes between 15 and 20 hours. But a schedule would show that a client who departs on January 1 would arrive on January 3. Explain why. (And explain what would happen if that client's birthday was on January 2.)

   _____

36. On a flight from Fiji to Tahiti, a client might depart on January 1 and arrive on December 31. Explain why.

   _____

37. Where in your area would you send your clients to get a passport?

   _____

38. When and why would you advise clients to take a transformer on their journey?

   _____

39. When and why would you advise clients to take an adapter on their journey?

   _____

40. What might you advise clients about the VAT in some countries?

   _____

Name _____   Date _____

Directions: Use the Internet to answer the following questions.

1. If you wanted to give a client an idea of how large France is, what state in the United States would you compare it to?

   _____

2. Choose a major European country. In what U.S. cities does this country have tourist offices?

   _____

   _____

3. When is the best time in terms of climate to go to Nigeria and why?

   _____

   _____

   _____

4. What are the temperature and precipitation today in Paris, France?

   _____

5. How many hours is Newfoundland ahead of your time zone?

   _____

Directions: For practice in going online to find out more about specific destinations, complete the following exercises.

6. Go to the Web site for DK Publishing (www.dk.com). Navigate through the site to find a list of their Eyewitness Travel Guides. List three of your favorite destinations covered by this guidebook series.

   a. _____

   b. _____

   c. _____

7. Go to the Web site for Fodor's guidebooks, and pick a city. Find a restaurant, and read how Fodor's reviews it. Summarize what you found in a few sentences.

   _____

   _____

   _____

   _____

(continued)

Directions: Use a Web site such as www.xe.com to obtain the following information for clients. Answers may differ slightly from one day to another.

8. The Centre Ville Etoile Hotel in Paris is listed at 110 euros. What is the price in U.S. dollars?

   _____

9. A half-day tour of a volcano and rain forest outside of San José costs 17,000 Costa Rican colones. How much will that cost your clients in U.S. dollars?

   _____

10. The bullet train from Tokyo to Osaka is listed at 15,500 yen. How much will that cost in U.S. dollars?

    _____

11. Your client cashes in a $100 traveler's check in Canada. How many Canadian dollars will he receive?

    _____

12. Your clients cash in a $100 traveler's check to pay for a dinner bill that comes to 500 pesos in Mexico City. How many pesos will you receive in change?

    _____

Name _____   Date _____

Directions: Consider the following issue. Conduct research to help you respond, and be prepared to discuss the topic in class.

Sustainable development and management of tourism

Tourism can bring many positive changes to a community, such as jobs, economic growth, and a higher standard of living, but tourism also can have harmful effects. What are some of the negative impacts that tourism can have that communities or countries need to guard against?

Find an example of an area that has experienced negative effects due to tourism. Describe these effects and address the following questions: Have people in the area taken steps to improve the situation? If so, what have they done? If not, what can be done? What resources do they have available to help them devise a plan? Specify the Web site(s) and other sources you used to formulate your essay.

_____

_____

_____

_____

_____

_____

_____

_____

_____

_____

_____

_____

_____

_____

_____

_____

_____

_____

_____

_____

_____

Name _____ Date _____

1. Amadeus _____

_____

2. Apollo _____

_____

3. Bricks-and-clicks agency _____

_____

4. Browser _____

_____

5. Command interface _____

_____

6. CRS _____

_____

7. Database _____

_____

8. Direct link _____

_____

9. Electronic reading device _____

_____

10. E-mail _____

_____

11. Galileo _____

_____

12. GDS _____

_____

13. Graphical interface _____

_____

(continued)

14. Hotspot _____

_____

15. Internet _____

_____

16. ISP _____

_____

17. Sabre _____

_____

18. Search engine _____

_____

19. Skype _____

_____

20. URL _____

_____

21. WiFi _____

_____

22. Worldspan _____

_____

23. World Wide Web _____

_____

Name   Date

Directions: Circle the letter indicating the best answer to each question.

1. Which of the following statements about GDSs is true?
   a. Today's GDSs can run a host of programs.
   b. Both command and graphical interfaces are available on GDSs.
   c. Companies can gain access to a GDS in several ways.
   d. All of the above are true.

2. A direct link between a supplier's computer system and the GDS
   a. ensures that the information on the GDS about the supplier's product is up-to-date.
   b. is not useful.
   c. exists for all suppliers that participate in a GDS.
   d. has become obsolete.

3. The information on a GDS
   a. is carefully regulated by the U.S. Department of Transportation.
   b. is closely regulated by the FCC.
   c. is no longer regulated by the federal government.
   d. is regulated by ARC.

4. Which GDS is owned by several European airlines?
   a. Sabre
   b. Galileo
   c. Amadeus
   d. Worldspan

5. A computer can be linked to the Internet through
   a. phone lines or cable.
   b. DSL or a satellite.
   c. a WiFi network.
   d. any of the above.

6. What would you set up if you wanted a messaging system accessible only to people within a company?
   a. A listserv
   b. A usenet
   c. A chat room
   d. An intranet

7. What is www.thetravelinstitute.com?
   a. A protocol for browsers
   b. A bulletin board
   c. An ISP
   d. A URL

8. What are Google, Bing, Yahoo, and Safari?
   a. URLs
   b. Bulletin boards
   c. Search engines
   d. GDSs

(continued)

Directions: Fill in the blanks.

9. Five tasks unrelated to airline travel that a CRS can perform are

   a. _____

   b. _____

   c. _____

   d. _____

   e. _____

10. Three reasons to use e-mail are

   a. _____

   b. _____

   c. _____

11. Web sites that are likely to offer research material on travel include those hosted by

   a. _____

   b. _____

   c. _____

   d. _____

12. When using the Internet for research, you should take three steps to ensure the quality of the information:

   a. _____

   b. _____

   c. _____

Name   Date

Directions: Indicate whether the following statements are true or false. If a statement is false, rewrite it to create a true statement.

1. Compared with a graphical interface, a command interface allows the user to enter information more quickly. True or false?

   _____

2. Linking information from a client database with information from an accounting system is easily done with integrated software. True or false?

   _____

3. Booking engines such as VAX VacationAccess allow travel agencies to book online more easily. True or false?

   _____

4. Dynamic packaging makes it easier for travel agencies to go online to create a travel package, book several types of travel components online, and offer clients a travel package with just a single overall price. True or false?

   _____

5. A back-office system such as TRAMS's ClientBase handles accounting and marketing tasks. True or false?

   _____

6. Today, most GDSs are owned and operated by the leading airlines. True or false?

   _____

7. Information on the Internet must be true or it couldn't be published there. True or false?

   _____

8. The Internet is used by a lot of "lookers" who can be turned into "bookers" by enterprising travel counselors. True or false?

   _____

9. Expedia and Travelocity are leading online travel agencies. True or false?

   _____

10. Many Web sites can offer a vast array of information on the Internet for free because companies pay to advertise on Web sites. True or false?

    _____

(continued)

11. A travel agency that has both a retail location and a strong Internet presence might be called a bricks-and-mortar agency. True or false?

_____

12. One important service that travel counselors can provide is to use their relationships with suppliers to verify information that clients find online. True or false?

_____

Name _____

Date _____

Directions: For practice using the Web sites that are prominent sources of information about the travel industry, complete the following exercises.

1. Enter "travel technology" in the Search box at *Travel Weekly*'s Web site. Choose an article that interests you and write a one-paragraph statement of what you learned from it.

   Article _____

   _____

   _____

   _____

   _____

2. Find and go to the Web site of one of the major GDSs; then choose one article from its press releases or other information sections. Summarize the article you have chosen in a sentence or two.

   Article _____

   _____

   _____

   _____

   _____

3. Go to two search engines of your choice (such as www.yahoo.com or www.google.com), and enter a travel-related topic that interests you into the Search box of each. How would you characterize the differences in the results?

   Search engines _____

   _____

   _____

   _____

4. Use a search engine to find the Web site of *National Geographic* magazine. What are the featured stories for this month?

   _____

   _____

   _____

(continued)

5. Use your favorite search engine to find the names of three dynamic packaging tools for travel agencies.

_____

_____

_____

Name _____ Date _____

Directions: Consider the following issue. Conduct research to help you respond, and be prepared to discuss the topic in class. (Tip: Refer to Web sites and other resources.)

Technology's impact on travel

Technology has changed the way the world conducts business. What are some of the ways technology has changed the travel industry? Some people predicted that the Internet would decrease the need for travel agents. In your opinion, has this happened? Why or why not? Write one or two paragraphs in response.

_____

_____

_____

_____

_____

_____

_____

_____

_____

_____

_____

_____

_____

_____

_____

_____

_____

_____

_____

Name   Date

Directions: Define the following terms.

1. Airline Deregulation Act 1978 ended the gov'ts economic control of U.S. Airliner airline determine their own Routes, fares, + commissions

2. ARC Airline Reporting Corporation. Regulate the distribution of airline tickets

3. APEX fare most frequent used discount fare for international travel. Advance Purchase Excursion.

4. Arrival tax individuals flying into the US or any of its possessions

5. ATA Air Transport Ass. trade ass. of major U.S. airline, to adopt a system remarkably similar to the one that existed during gov't reg

6. Boarding pass allows passenger to board flight

7. Buffer zone 225 mile that extends from the US border into Canada + Mexico

8. Bulkhead divide the plane into compartments, + the airline offers different classes of service in the department compartments.

9. Bumped not enough seats so passengers cannot board

10. Business class drinks may be free + the seating is in a quieter area than the coach section.

11. Charter specially scheduled flights reserved by a private group or tour operator.

12. Circle trip like a round-trip except that the Route on the Return trip differs from the Route on the outgoing trip.

(continued)

13. Civil aviation includes all air service that is offered to the public for hire, whether for passangers or for cargo.

14. Classes of service First class and coach.

15. Coach fly discount fares

16. Code-sharing agreements allow airlines to use the code of a larger, better-known airline. Call companies to coordinate their schedules + marketing efforts.

17. Commuter airline small regional airlines. generate annual operating revenues less than $100 mil. Offer service only to one region of the country.

18. Configuration layout of seats

19. Confirmed reserved flights

20. Connecting flight a stop that requires the passanger to change planes.

21. Connection stop occurs when the passenger gets off aplane with the sole purpose of boarding another plane.

22. Consolidator distribution companies that negotiate w/ airlines to buy seats on international flights at bargain rates

23. Construction principles used in calculating mileage-based fares.

24. Denied boarding compensation if the airline cannot get a bumped passenger to destination within 1 hour

25. Departure tax on individuals flying out of the US or any of its possessions

(continued)

Name _____   Date _____

26. Direct flight _One or more stops at which the passenger does not have to change planes._

27. Discount fare _____

28. Domestic air travel _includes flights between and within the continental US and parts of Puerto Rico, Virgin Islands, + Canada_

29. Double open-jaw trip _more than one airport in the city._

30. Economy class _the coach on international flights._

31. Electronic ticket _not printed only on a computer or phone_

32. Excess baggage charge _varies from airline to airline_

33. Executive class _just like business_

34. FAA _Federal aviation administration Est 1958 to license pilots, certify aircraft as safe, + enforce rules regarding passenger safety._

35. First class _more legroom, seats are wider, seperate check-in, more flight attendants, free alcohol_

36. Frequent-flyer plan _bonus program._

37. Gateway _cities that serve as arrival or departure points for international travel._

38. HIP _fare between 2 cities on an itinerary is higher than the through fare between the origin + the destination. Passenger pays higher fare._

(continued)

39. Hub-and-spoke system airline uses certain cities as connecting centers for as many flights to and from outlying cities as possible.

40. IATA Est 1919. 230 international airlines. Aims to create order + stability in international aviation. International Air Transport Association.

41. IATAN 1985 Replaced IATA as org. that appoints US travel agencies to sell tickets for international airlines serving the U.S.

42. Interline agreement aspects of travel are governed by agreements among the airlines themselves. Ex: airline ticketing

43. Joint fare connection involves different airlines that agree on one published fare

44. Mileage system fare depends on 1. origin 2. farthest point on the trip 3. number of miles flown.

45. MPM passengers wish to make stops that bring the trip over a certain allotted number of miles. Pay through fare plus a surcharge.

46. Nonstop flight no intermediate stops

47. No-show people don't cancel or change reservation, but don't show up.

48. NTSB Est 1967 to investigate accidents, and the FAA became of the DOT. National Transportation Safety Board

49. NUC special counting units

50. One-way trip journey from an originating city to a destination city, with no return to the origin.

51. Open-jaw trip like round-trip except the passenger either 1. returns to a different city or 2. departs for the return trip from a city other than the original.

(continued)

Name   Date

52. Open-skies policy 1990's gov't urged. Carriers can fly where they choose, charge what they wish, + make deals with each other

53. Overbook Sell more tickets than seats in order to compensate for no-shows

54. Oversold # of confirmed passengers who show up for flight is over # of seats.

55. Paper ticket the percentage of available seats on a flight that is actually sold. Would be extremely small.

56. Passenger load factor percentage of available seats on a flight that are actually sold

57. PFC Passenger Facility Charge. levied at almost all US airports. FAA allows airports to collect surcharge for airport improvements.

58. Pitch leg room

59. PNR Passenger name record, complete record of a reservation stored by the airline's reservation system.

60. Point-to-point fare fares from one stopover point to another. Usually more expensive.

61. Promotional fare airline may offer a lower fare when it opens a new route, promote during off-season, competition.

62. Rate desk part of an airline or travel agency staffed by specialists in international airfares.

63. Record locator number for each PNR the computer assigns a record locator #, a combination of #s/letters that is used to retrieve the PNR.

64. Round-trip journey returns to the city where it began, without additional stopovers.

65. Routing system the fare depends on the specific route flown

66. Scheduled service consists of flights for designated routes offered to the public according to a publishe timetable

67. Seat width total side-to-side space at seat cushion or chest level

68. Security fee Est 2001. to pay for increased security measures.

69. Segment tax charged for each takeoff + landing

70. Standard ticket Let passengers fly on many airlines w/ just one ticket

71. Standby waitlisted only until day of the flight

72. Stop when a plane stops

73. Stopover a planned break in a journey

74. Through fare fare through a connecting point between same airlines.

75. Through flight one or more stops at which the passenger does not have to change planes.

76. TSA Transportation Security Admin. 2001 airport security became a direct federal responsibility.

77. U.S. ticket tax Federal transportation tax charged on tickets purchased within the US when air travel meets 1. within US 2. within Alaska + Hawaii 3. between US and a 225-mile buffer zone 4. within buffer zone.

(continued)

Name   Date

78. Waitlisted _If no space is available, put on a list of people seeking a sold-out service._

79. Yield _Average amount of revenue earned per passenger mile; it is computed by dividing total passenger revenue by the total number of passenger miles flown._

80. Yield management system _____

Name _____ Date _____

Directions: Answer the following questions in the space provided.

1. What were the effects of the Airline Deregulation Act of 1978 on each of the following?

   a. Airlines _____

   _____

   b. Travel counselors _____

   _____

   c. Consumers _____

   _____

2. Name one advantage and one disadvantage of the hub-and-spoke system from the viewpoint of the airlines.

   _____

   _____

3. Name one advantage and one disadvantage of the hub-and-spoke system for travelers.

   _____

   _____

4. What are some key benefits offered by airline-sponsored members-only lounges?

   _____

   _____

5. Why should travel counselors be aware of code sharing by airlines, and what should they do about it?

   _____

   _____

   _____

6. What should travel counselors advise clients about security and check-in times?

   _____

   _____

   _____

(continued)

Directions: Circle the letter indicating the best answer to each question.

7. The primary function of the FAA is
   a. to ensure that the airline system is regulated financially.
   b. to settle strikes and make certain that the airlines keep flying.
   c. to enforce rules regarding passenger safety.
   d. to see that travelers are not overcharged for tickets.

8. The FAA is a division of the
   a. NTSB.
   b. ARC.
   c. CAB.
   d. DOT.

9. What airline organization do travel agencies deal with most frequently?
   a. FAA
   b. ARC
   c. ATA
   d. DOT

Name _____   Date _____

Directions: Fill in the airport and airline codes.

Airport	Code
1. Boston, MA	_____
2. Detroit, MI/Wayne County	_____
3. Dallas, TX	_____
4. Kansas City, MO	_____
5. Los Angeles, CA/Burbank	_____
6. St. Louis, MO	_____
7. Pittsburgh, PA	_____
8. Salt Lake City, UT	_____
9. Denver, CO	_____
10. Atlanta, GA	_____
11. Minneapolis, MN	_____
12. Chicago, IL/Midway	_____
13. Cleveland, OH	_____
14. Orlando, FL/International	_____
15. Mexico City, MX	_____
16. Washington, DC/Dulles	_____
17. Richmond, VA	_____
18. Charleston, SC	_____
19. Phoenix, AZ	_____
20. Seattle, WA	_____
21. Milwaukee, WI	_____
22. Ottawa, Ont.	_____
23. Indianapolis, IN	_____
24. Little Rock, AR	_____

(continued)

Airport	Code
25. Nassau, Bahamas	_____
26. New Orleans, LA	_____

Airline	Code
27. United Airlines	_____
28. US Airways	_____
29. American Airlines	_____
30. Delta Airlines	_____
31. Hawaiian Airlines	_____
32. Southwest Airlines	_____
33. Alaska Airlines	_____
34. Frontier Airlines	_____
35. Jet Blue	_____

Name _____   Date _____

Directions: List the major gateway city for each country and the major airport code(s) for that city.

Country	Major gateway city	Major airport code
1. England	_____	_____
	_____	_____
2. France	_____	_____
	_____	_____
3. India	_____	_____
4. Egypt	_____	_____
5. Netherlands	_____	_____
6. Austria	_____	_____
7. Italy	_____	_____
	_____	_____
8. Spain	_____	_____
9. Ireland	_____	_____
	_____	_____
10. Argentina	_____	_____
11. China	_____	_____
12. Australia	_____	_____
13. Japan	_____	_____
14. Russia	_____	_____
15. Costa Rica	_____	_____

Directions: Name the flag carriers of the countries listed and give their two-letter codes.

Country	Flag carrier (airline)	Airline code
16. Israel	_____	_____
17. Mexico	_____	_____
18. Germany	_____	_____

(continued)

Name _____   Date _____

Directions: Today is January 1. An airfare has been announced by International Airways for $399 (slightly higher on Friday to Sunday) round-trip from your major city to Rome on direct flights. The fare has a 7-day minimum/30-day maximum stay. It must be booked 7 days in advance, and it must be ticketed within 1 day of booking. A $100 cancellation or change fee applies. The fare sale ends January 15 and is for travel from January 1 to March 31. Blackout dates are February 12 and March 17. The number of seats is capacity controlled, and interlining is not allowed.

Answer "Yes" or "No" to the following questions. If the answer is "No," describe what you would do or say to the client to make him or her eligible for the fare and to make the sale.

1. A client calls today and wants to travel from February 13 to March 13. Will she be eligible for the fare?

   _____

   _____

2. A client calls today and wants to travel from January 17 to February 17. Will she be eligible for the fare?

   _____

   _____

3. A client calls on January 17 and wants to travel from March 18 to March 30. Will she be eligible for the fare?

   _____

   _____

4. A client calls on January 10 and wants to travel from January 15 to January 31. Will she be eligible for the fare?

   _____

   _____

5. A client calls today and says she must travel on January 31 and return on February 14. She is told that the seats are sold out but that she can travel on the same flights on the same days for $599. She insists that she be given the $399 fare because it is obvious that seats are available. Will she prevail in her argument?

   _____

   _____

6. A client calls today and wants to travel on March 4 and return March 11. He wants to book a connection through Paris on the return (the airline does have a connecting schedule) in order to purchase something at the duty-free shop in the Paris airport. Will he be eligible for the fare?

   _____

   _____

(continued)

7. Universal Airlines is offering the same fare as International Airways and has flight times on the return that are better for one particular client. Will he be eligible for the fare if he takes International on the outbound flight and Universal on the return?

   _____

   _____

8. A client calls on January 10 and makes a reservation to travel between March 1 and March 14 and says that he will come in the next day with his payment for ticketing. The next day he comes in and decides to change his return from March 14 to March 15. Will he be eligible for the fare?

   _____

   _____

9. A client calls on January 10 and wants to travel from February 28 to March 17. By what day must he be ticketed to be eligible for the fare?

   _____

   _____

10. A client calls on January 15 and wants to travel between January 22 and January 29. By what day must he be ticketed to be eligible for the fare?

    _____

    _____

Name _____   Date _____

Directions: Answer the following questions.

1. What are three benefits of traveling first class?

   a. _____

   b. _____

   c. _____

2. What is one circumstance in which you would waitlist a client on a flight?

   _____

3. What are the advantages of "ticketless travel" to the airlines? To passengers?

   _____

   _____

4. What is your preferred place to sit on a plane and why?

   _____

   _____

5. Passengers holding ticket/boarding passes are automatically guaranteed a seat on their flight no matter when they arrive at the gate. True or false?

   _____

6. Airlines must provide compensation for clients involuntarily bumped from flights. True or false?

   _____

7. It is illegal for airlines to overbook flights. True or false?

   _____

8. Business or executive classes range somewhere between first class and coach in amenities. True or false?

   _____

9. Special meals on a flight need to be ordered at least 12 to 24 hours in advance. True or false?

   _____

10. What is the difference between a wide-bodied and a narrow-bodied plane?

    _____

(continued)

11. If you were a travel counselor or airline reservations agent helping a first-time flyer select a seat, how would you summarize the pros and cons of these seating options?

    a. Over the wings

    _____

    _____

    _____

    b. Emergency exit rows

    _____

    _____

    _____

    c. Middle rows

    _____

    _____

    _____

    d. Aisle seats

    _____

    _____

    _____

    e. Bulkhead seats

    _____

    _____

    _____

12. What is an airline rate desk? What service does it offer travel counselors?

    _____

    _____

    _____

(continued)

Name   Date

13. What is the major advantage to travelers having their international air tickets booked through a consolidator rather than directly through an airline?

_____

_____

_____

14. What are three disadvantages to booking international air tickets through a consolidator?

  a. _____

  b. _____

  c. _____

15. What are two major advantages to travelers in taking a charter?

  a. Advantages_____

  b. Disadvantages_____

Directions: Circle the letter indicating the best answer to each question.

16. On international flights, the charge for an infant not occupying a seat is generally
  a. half of the adult fare, regardless of the discount on the fare.
  b. one-quarter of the adult fare.
  c. 10 percent of the adult fare.
  d. nothing; infants fly free.

17. The standard term on international flights for what is called coach class on U.S. domestic flights is
  a. economy.
  b. second.
  c. open.
  d. steerage.

Name _____   Date _____

Directions: Choose a major U.S. city pair for a round-trip itinerary. (You might choose a destination that you or someone you know is actually planning to visit.) Find the best round-trip fare available between those two cities regardless of dates by going to each of the following: (a) either Travelocity or Expedia, (b) Orbitz, and (c) a major U.S. airline's Web site.

Destination _____

1. What airfares did you find?

   a. _____

   b. _____

   c. _____

2. When searching for the fares, what difference did you encounter among the Web sites?

   _____

   _____

   _____

3. Which site would be your first choice if you were to use one of them for your next trip?

   _____

Directions: Practice finding travel-related information online by completing the following exercises.

4. Summarize a news release or announcement on ARC's Web site (www.arccorp.com) in a sentence or two.

   _____

   _____

   _____

5. List three topics and their section numbers from the "Industry Agent's Handbook" at ARC's Web site.

   a. _____

   b. _____

   c. _____

6. What are the on-time statistics for airlines at the largest airport close to you? (Tip: Go to www.faa.gov.)

   _____

(continued)

7. Choose one topic that interests you from the Department of Homeland Security's Web site (www.dhs.gov), and summarize it in a sentence or two.

   _____

   _____

   _____

8. Choose one topic that interests you at the Air Transport Association's Web site (www.airlines.org), and summarize it in a sentence or two.

   _____

   _____

   _____

   _____

Directions: Complete the following exercises for practice in finding information about international travel at prominent Web sites.

9. Choose a major international city and a U.S. city for a round-trip itinerary. Check airfares for three months from now by going to three Web sites: (a) either Travelocity or Expedia, (b) Orbitz, and (c) a major U.S. airline's Web site.

Itinerary _____

   a. _____

   b. _____

   c. _____

10. Go to a consolidator's Web site (try www.airlineconsolidator.com) for the same round-trip itinerary that you checked in the previous exercise. Compare the fares and the restrictions on scheduling or other rules described on the consolidator's Web site with those you found in the previous question.

   _____

   _____

11. Go to the Web site for the U.S. State Department (www.travel.state.gov). How many travel warnings or alerts are posted today? Summarize one.

   _____

   _____

   _____

(continued)

Name   Date

_____

12. Choose one region of the world. Then go to the Web site of the Centers for Disease Control and Prevention to determine the special precautions that a client must take when traveling to that region. Summarize your findings.

_____

_____

_____

Name _____   Date _____

Directions: Consider the following concepts and issues. Conduct research to help you respond, and be prepared to discuss the topic in class.

New business model: low-cost carriers

Low-cost airlines are establishing and providing air service in many areas across the globe. Many of these carriers are actually making a profit at a time when the major long-standing airlines are financially strapped and losing money. How is this possible? What do the low-cost carriers do that the major airlines have been unable to do? Find and research a few of their Web sites.

Write a paragraph or two that lists their strategies and describes how they differ from the major airlines.

Major	Low
using multiple plane sizes	use minimal plane sizes = less training + maintenance costs
have hub locations	no free meals or drinks
	shorter routes
	stay away from busy expensive hubs allow more trips → less delays
	sold through direct web = No commission cost

Name _____   Date _____

Directions: Define the following terms.

1. AAA A motor club that offers members a variety of travel and motoring services

2. Acela Express Amtrak's high speed train serving the Northeast corridor of the US

3. ALI extra coverage for injury, death, or other liability to a 3rd party, beyond both what state law mandates that car rental companies include in the cost of the rental and what the renter's own insurance might cover.

4. Amtrak the corporation that operates intercity passenger rail service in the US

5. BritRail pass A rail pass that allows travel throughout England, Scotland, + Wales

6. Bullet train Japan's high-speed passenger train

7. Canrailpass A pass offered by VIA Rail that provides 12 days of unlimited travel anywhere in Canada during a 30-day period.

8. Chunnel tunnel beneath the English Channel that links England and France

9. CDW Insurance that waives the car rental company's right to charge the renter for damages if the rental car is involved in an accident

10. Couchette Sleeping accommodations on a train consisting of a compartment with 6 bunk beds; found on European trains

11. ELI Adds insurance for injuries to persons or property up to $1 million above what is covered by the renter's own car insurance

12. Eurailpass Est 1959. allows unlimited 1st-class travel through 23 European countries for a specified time

(continued)

13. Eurostar operates through the chunnel. Tunnel beneath the English Channel

14. IDP translation of the bearer's driver's license into an internationally recognized format. International Driver's Permit

15. LDW waives the rental company's right to recover damages resulting from theft or vandalism as well as from collisions. Loss Damage Waiver

16. Motorcoach coach bus

17. PAI covers bodily injury to the car renter. Personal Accident Insurance

18. Point-to-point tickets vary in price based on 1. advance purchase 2. time of day 3. # of changes 4. type of equipment on route

19. Rail Europe A company owned by Swiss & French railroads that acts as a U.S. booking agent for virtually all trains in Europe.

20. Rail pass allow train travel for a specified time and region with unlimited stops and unlimited mileage.

21. Specialty train trains taken for the experience, not the transportation

22. TGV train à grande vitesse. travel 200 miles per hour

23. Transfers transportation between hotels, airports, docks, or railroad stations.

24. USA Rail pass variety of options. 8 segments within 15 days, 12 segments within 30 days, 18 segments within 45 days. purchase ≠ reservation

25. VIA Rail Canada's passenger train network, cross between the 2 nations

Name   Date

Directions: Indicate whether the following statements are true or false. If a statement is false, rewrite it to create a true statement.

1. Amtrak trains offer sleeping accommodations on all routes. True or false?

   _____

2. Most trains in Europe offer only one class of service. True or false?

   _____

3. Eurail Global Passes can be purchased at any train station in Europe. True or false?

   _____

4. Most car renters need to pay for damage and collision insurance at the time of rental. True or false?

   _____

5. Eurostar operates under the Irish Sea uniting England and Ireland. True or false?

   _____

6. Rail passes by themselves do not guarantee a seat. True or false?

   _____

Directions: Provide the information requested.

7. Name three advantages of traveling by rail rather than car.

   a. _____

   b. _____

   c. _____

8. Name three advantages of traveling by car rather than rail.

   a. _____

   b. _____

   c. _____

(continued)

9. Name five ways in which full-service car rental companies try to give better service than their counterparts.

    a. _____

    b. _____

    c. _____

    d. _____

    e. _____

10. Identify four differences between renting a car in another country and renting one in the United States.

    a. _____

    b. _____

    c. _____

    d. _____

Directions: For each train, identify the continent on which it travels: Africa, Asia, Australia, Europe, North America, or South America.

11. *The Copper Canyon* _____

12. *The Orient Express* _____

13. *The Palace on Wheels* _____

14. *The Blue Train* _____

15. *The Cascades* _____

16. *TGV* _____

Name   Date

Directions: Refer to various appropriate Web sites to find the information to handle the following scenarios.

1. Abel Adams is a budget traveler who is arriving in London on July 1. He is staying in the city for four nights and then wants to travel by rail throughout all of England, seeing as much as he can of the country and the countryside. He will depart for home on July 27. Which pass would you recommend and why?

2. Betsy Baker is arriving in Edinburgh on August 25. She will stay for one week, attending events at the Edinburgh Festival, and then would like to explore Scotland by train for two weeks, traveling every other day.

   a. Which rail pass would you recommend, and why?

   b. Can Betsy take a train to Glasgow airport? Explain.

3. Upon arriving at London/Heathrow airport, Abel Adams wants to take a train into downtown London.

   a. What is the name of the train?   _____

   b. How long will it take?   _____

   c. How much does a first-class ticket cost?   _____

4. What Web site will you consult for detailed up-to-the-minute train times for Abel and Betsy?

5. Cornell Corman and David Donaldson want to have a five-day stay in Paris at the start of their trip and a five-day stay in Rome at the end of their trip. They'll be away from June 1 through June 30. In between they wish to travel by train to as many locales and countries in Europe as time allows. What rail pass will you recommend to them?

6. Ed Eagleton is going to spend one week each in Paris, Berlin, Rome, Florence, Zurich, and Madrid to study the architecture. He would like to travel by first-class train between cities. (He will fly into Paris and return home from Madrid.) Which pass will you recommend to him, and why?

7. Frances and Frank are a retired couple (in their sixties) who want to travel throughout France for a month, seeing Paris, Strasbourg, Lyon, Nice, Marseille, Bordeaux, and Nantes. What pass will you recommend for them?

(continued)

Directions: Use Web sites to complete the following exercises.

8. Compare the one-day rates for a standard (full-size) car at New York/LaGuardia airport for the first Tuesday in August offered by Hertz and Budget car rental companies.

 a. Hertz _____

 b. Budget _____

9. Compare the one-day rates for a standard (full-size) car at Orlando airport for the first Tuesday in November offered by Avis and Alamo car rental companies.

 a. Avis _____

 b. Alamo _____

Name   Date

Directions: Consider the following concepts and issues. Conduct research to help you respond, and be prepared to discuss the topic in class.

The Future of Passenger Rail in the United States

Americans love their cars. The passenger rail service in the United States, although improving, cannot compare with the efficient rail systems in other parts of the world. Some Americans think that this is about to change. There has been an increase in light-rail systems across the nation, and many cities are considering proposals for inter-city commuter rails. What do you think? Will Americans become less dependent on their cars and turn to the rails? List the advantages and disadvantages of increased development of the passenger rail system in the United States.

_____

_____

_____

_____

_____

_____

_____

_____

_____

_____

_____

_____

_____

_____

_____

_____

_____

_____

_____

_____

Name _____ Date _____

Directions: Define the following terms.

1. Adjoining rooms _____

   _____

2. AH&LA _____

   _____

3. Airport hotel _____

   _____

4. All-inclusive _____

   _____

5. All-suite _____

   _____

6. AP _____

   _____

7. B&B _____

   _____

8. Boatel _____

   _____

9. BP _____

   _____

10. Brand _____

    _____

11. Casino _____

    _____

12. Chain _____

    _____

(continued)

13. Château, castle, and villa _____

_____

14. Commercial hotel _____

_____

15. Concierge _____

_____

16. Connecting rooms _____

_____

17. Convention hotel _____

_____

18. Convention rate _____

_____

19. Corporate rate _____

_____

20. CP _____

_____

21. Demi-pension _____

_____

22. Dine-around plan _____

_____

23. Dude ranch _____

_____

24. EP _____

_____

25. Extended-stay hotel _____

_____

(continued)

Name   Date

26. Franchise company _____

_____

27. Frequent-guest program _____

_____

28. Full board _____

_____

29. Group rate _____

_____

30. Guaranteed for late arrival _____

_____

31. Hold time _____

_____

32. Hospitality industry _____

_____

33. Hostel _____

_____

34. Hotel consolidator _____

_____

35. Hotel representative firm _____

_____

36. Inn _____

_____

37. Lodge _____

_____

38. Lodging _____

_____

(continued)

39. Management contract _____

_____

40. MAP _____

_____

41. Market segment _____

_____

42. Membership organization _____

_____

43. Minshuku _____

_____

44. Motel _____

_____

45. Motor inn _____

_____

46. Negotiated corporate rate _____

_____

47. Net rate _____

_____

48. Occupancy rate _____

_____

49. Parador _____

_____

50. Pension _____

_____

51. Pousada _____

_____

(continued)

Name _____ Date _____

52. Properties _____

_____

53. Rack rate _____

_____

54. Rep firm _____

_____

55. Resort _____

_____

56. Retreat-style accommodation _____

_____

57. Rondavel _____

_____

58. ROH _____

_____

59. Ryokan _____

_____

60. Self-catering rental apartment _____

_____

61. Spa _____

_____

62. Tented camp _____

_____

63. Tourist court _____

_____

64. Tree lodge _____

_____

(continued)

65. Walking the guest _____

_____

Name _____   Date _____

Directions: For the each of the following kinds of accommodations, briefly describe its distinguishing features and the types of travelers that it best suits.

	Features	**Types of travelers**
1. Motel	_____	_____
2. Commercial hotel	_____	_____
3. Convention hotel	_____	_____
4. Airport hotel	_____	_____
5. All-suite	_____	_____
6. Resort	_____	_____
7. Spa	_____	_____
8. All-inclusive	_____	_____
9. Bed-and-breakfast	_____	_____
10. Inn	_____	_____
11. Hostel	_____	_____

(continued)

Directions: For each type of accommodation, indicate the country with which it is most often associated.

12. Gasthaus	_____	a. Africa
13. Minshukus	_____	b. France
14. B&B	_____	c. Germany
15. Motel	_____	d. India
16. Pension	_____	e. Japan
17. Pousada	_____	f. Portugal
18. Parador	_____	g. Spain
19. Rondavel	_____	h. United Kingdom
20. Ryokan	_____	i. United States

Directions: Match the meal plan in the right column with the correct description in the left column.

21. No meals at all	_____	a. AP
22. Small breakfast	_____	b. BP
23. Full American breakfast	_____	c. CP
24. Two meals a day	_____	d. EP
25. Three meals a day	_____	e. MAP

Directions: Indicate which meal plan is most likely to be found at each hotel described at the left. (There are many exceptions to these answers; choose the most likely meal plan.)

26. Caribbean resort	_____	a. AP
27. Standard first-class hotel in the United States	_____	b. BP
		c. CP
28. A B&B	_____	d. EP
29. Secluded resort or ranch-resort	_____	e. MAP
30. Small hotel or pension in Italy, Spain, or France	_____	

Name _____   Date _____

Directions: Refer to the Web sites of the Hyatt-Regency Aruba Resort & Casino and the Divi Aruba All Inclusive to answer the following questions.

	Hyatt Regency	**Divi Aruba**
1. How many rooms are in the hotel?	_____	_____
2. How many miles is it from the airport?	_____	_____
3. What credit cards are accepted?	_____	_____
4. What is the hotel's classification?	_____	_____
5. When was the hotel built?	_____	_____
6. Does it have a beach?	_____	_____

7. At which hotel would you prefer to stay? Why?

_____

_____

8. Which would you recommend to a honeymoon couple? Why?

_____

_____

9. Which would you recommend to a young couple looking for lots of activity? Why?

_____

_____

10. Which would you book for a family of four (with two children 12 and 7)? Why?

_____

_____

Name   Date

Directions: Answer the following questions.

1. What are two advantages of lodgings that are part of a chain?

   a. _____

   b. _____

2. What are five ways of segmenting the accommodations market?

   a. _____

   b. _____

   c. _____

   d. _____

   e. _____

3. What are five characteristics that affect the price of a hotel room?

   a. _____

   b. _____

   c. _____

   d. _____

   e. _____

4. What is the responsibility of a hotel if it is oversold and a room is not available for someone with a guaranteed reservation?

   _____

   _____

5. What are three major hotel reference guides or Web sites, and what kinds of information does each provide?

   a. _____

   _____

   b. _____

   _____

   c. _____

   _____

Name   Date

Directions: Go to the Web site for the Fairmont Hotel in San Francisco.

1. How large a convention could the Fairmont Hotel accommodate for a reception in its ballroom?

2. What is the minimum rate for a twin?

3. On which of San Francisco's many hills is the hotel located?

4. How many guest rooms and suites does it have?

5. Who was its famous female architect after the destruction of the 1906 earthquake and fire?

6. What type of client might be ideal for this hotel?

7. Would it be a good choice for a business person attending a convention at the city's convention center, Moscone Center? Why or why not?

8. Does the Fairmont company have other properties in the United States? If so, where?

(continued)

Directions: Examine the following Web sites:

www.travelocity.com

www.expedia.com

www.hotels.com

www.localhotels.com

www.experienceispa.com

9. As a travel counselor, would you be most likely to use www.travelocity.com, www.expedia.com, or www.hotels.com to book a hotel? Why?

_____

_____

_____

_____

10. How might you use www.hotels.com and www.localhotels.com as a travel counselor?

_____

_____

_____

_____

11. At www.experienceispa.com, find and list the general types of spas.

_____

_____

_____

_____

12. Would you use www.experienceispa.com as a travel counselor? Why or why not?

_____

_____

_____

_____

Name   Date

Directions: Consider the following concepts and issues. Conduct research to help you respond, and be prepared to discuss the topic in class.

Hotel Classifications

Choosing the right hotel for each client is critical to the customers' satisfaction of their travel experience. It can be a challenge to assess the quality of hotels without knowing the property and without an official (government) classification system in the United States. Travel professionals should check several sources to verify the quality of accommodations.

Be prepared to discuss the advantages and disadvantages of an official hotel rating system.

1. List several of these sources and the pros and cons of each:

_____

_____

_____

_____

_____

_____

_____

_____

_____

_____

_____

_____

_____

_____

_____

_____

_____

_____

_____

_____

_____

Name _____   Date _____

Directions: Define the following terms.

1. Adventure cruise _____

   _____

2. Aft _____

   _____

3. Air/sea _____

   _____

4. Bareboat charter _____

   _____

5. Berth _____

   _____

6. Block_____

   _____

7. Bow _____

   _____

8. Cabin _____

   _____

9. CLIA _____

   _____

10. Country of registry _____

    _____

11. Cruise ship _____

    _____

12. Deck plan _____

    _____

(continued)

13. Embarkation point _____

_____

14. Expedition _____

_____

15. Ferry _____

_____

16. Flag of convenience _____

_____

17. Fly/cruise _____

_____

18. Fore _____

_____

19. Freighter _____

_____

20. Green sheet _____

_____

21. GRT _____

_____

22. Guaranteed rate _____

_____

23. Guaranteed share rate _____

_____

24. Hotel manager _____

_____

25. Knot _____

_____

(continued)

Name _____   Date _____

26. Megaship _____

_____

27. Niche cruises _____

_____

28. Option date _____

_____

29. Pitch _____

_____

30. Port charges _____

_____

31. Port of call _____

_____

32. Purser _____

_____

33. Repositioning cruise _____

_____

34. Roll _____

_____

35. Schooner _____

_____

36. Single supplement _____

_____

37. SOLAS _____

_____

38. Space ratio _____

_____

(continued)

39. Spread _____

_____

40. Stabilizer _____

_____

41. Stern _____

_____

42. Tender _____

_____

43. Third/fourth person rate _____

_____

44. Value season _____

_____

45. Windjammer _____

_____

46. Yacht _____

_____

Name   Date

Directions: Go to page 234 to view "A Cruise Itinerary" for Holland America's "Grand World Voyage," a 99-day voyage on the *Amsterdam*. Use an atlas to locate the stops on the cruise.

1. Choose one of the ports of call on the *Amsterdam*'s cruise, and research that port's main features and attractions. Construct a shore excursion of one day's duration that would take in those features and attractions. Use any travel resources available.

_____

_____

_____

_____

_____

_____

_____

_____

_____

_____

_____

_____

_____

_____

_____

_____

_____

_____

_____

_____

_____

(continued)

Directions: List the month or months during which cruises are popular in the following cruising areas.

Destination

2. Bermuda _____

_____

3. Hawaii _____

_____

4. Caribbean _____

_____

5. The Mediterranean _____

_____

6. Scandinavian fjords _____

_____

7. Alaska _____

_____

Name   Date

Directions: Use the Holland America Web site as a source of information to answer the following questions.

1. List 5 ports that Holland America's Canada/New England cruises depart from.

   _____

   _____

   _____

   _____

   _____

2. What is the Mariner Society and who is eligible to belong?

   _____

   _____

   _____

   _____

3. Are wheelchairs provided for guests onboard and for shore excursions? Are personal mobility scooters allowed onboard?

   _____

   _____

   _____

4. When are deposits generally due? Final payment?

   _____

   _____

5. What currencies are accepted onboard Holland America ships?

   _____

   _____

6. What is the recommended way to check in for a cruise, and when should the process be completed?

   _____

   _____

7. What is the ratio of crew members to guests?

_____

8. Does Holland America offer any youth programs on their ships? Briefly explain.

_____

_____

_____

_____

9. How many ships are in the Holland America fleet?

_____

10. a. If you buy a standard Cancellation Protection Plan, what percent of your payment will be refunded?

_____

   b. What is the latest that the cancellation can be made to receive a refund under the standard plan? How must the cruise line be notified of a cancellation?

_____

_____

   c. What plan reimburses up to $10,000 in medical expenses if you become sick or injured on your vacation? What other medical expenses are covered?

_____

_____

_____

_____

Name _____ Date _____

Directions: Use the Holland America Web site as a source of information to answer the following questions. First click on the "Find Cruises" tab near the top of the screen. On the next screen, choose "Alaska (all)" from the pulldown menu at the "Choose Destination" block, and click the "View Itineraries" button. Use this information to make the following comparisons between cruises.

	7-Day Inside Passage	**7-Day Alaskan Explorer**
1. Departure port	_____	_____
2. Arrival port	_____	_____
3. Tracy Arm visited?	_____	_____
4. Number of ports visited	_____	_____
5. Ship(s) used	_____	_____
	_____	_____
	_____	_____
6. Cost of Ocean-view stateroom	_____	_____
7. Departure days	_____	_____
	_____	_____
	_____	_____

8. Choose one shore excursion that interests you and describe its appeal.

_____

_____

_____

_____

_____

_____

_____

_____

_____

Name   Date

Directions: Indicate whether the following statements are true or false. If part or all of the statement is false, explain why.

1. Cruising is mostly for senior citizens. True or false?

   _____

2. The longer the cruise, the older the passengers tend to be. True or false?

   _____

3. Cruises are popular, but they cost substantially more than land vacations. True or false?

   _____

4. Many cruises tend to be informal, with just one or two dress-up nights a week. True or false?

   _____

5. Cruises are a good way to see an island or an area in depth and to get to know its culture. True or false?

   _____

Directions: Answer the following questions.

6. Circle all of the following features that are *not* included in the basic price of *most* major cruises.

   (a) Meals   (b) Tips   (c) Port taxes   (d) Nightclub entertainment   (e) Sightseeing

   (f) Liquor   (g) Soft drinks   (h) Room (cabin) service   (i) Movies   (j) Transfers

7. What are four benefits of cruising?

   a. _____

   b. _____

   c. _____

   d. _____

8. What are two possible disadvantages of cruising?

   a. _____

   b. _____

(continued)

9. What are four factors that determine the price of a cruise?

    a. _____

    b. _____

    c. _____

    d. _____

10. Why might a client prefer an inside cabin?

    _____

    _____

11. What are three great rivers that lend themselves to cruising?

    _____

12. To what types of travelers might you suggest the first sitting?

    _____

Name   Date

Directions: Find CLIA's Web site, and then complete the following exercises.

1. Enter your zip code at the "Cruise Expert Finder" section of CLIA's Web site. Write the names of the travel agencies in your area that are CLIA affiliates.

   _____

   _____

2. CLIA's "Cruise Lines & Ships" lists cruise line members. Name two that offer group fitness classes and personal trainers.

   _____

   _____

3. You have a client who would like to cruise with his wife and two teenagers. Choose five cruise lines that offer a teen center or disco onboard.

   a. _____

   b. _____

   c. _____

   d. _____

   e. _____

4. How many new ships are on order by CLIA members for the 2013–2015 period?

   _____

5. Name at least three governmental agencies that interact with CLIA's Executive Partner program.

   _____

   _____

   _____

Directions: To gain practice in exploring other Web sites that help you learn about and sell cruises, complete the following exercises.

6. Go to the Web site of *Porthole* magazine. Choose one of the news articles in the "Cruise News" section, and list its topic.

   _____

(continued)

7. Find the Web site of the International Council of Cruise Lines. Choose one interesting fact about cruising in the site's "Cruise Industry FAQs." Write the fact here, and be prepared to relate it to your fellow students.

_____

_____

_____

8. Is it possible for clients to book their shore excursions before departure on Royal Caribbean Cruise Line? What stipulations must they follow? See www.royalcaribbean.com. Click on "Before You Board," and then click on "Shore & Land Excursions."

_____

_____

_____

Name   Date

Directions: Consider the following concepts and issues. Conduct research to help you respond, and be prepared to discuss the topic in class.

From Dying to Thriving

Passenger ocean liner travel was a dying industry once jet service across the Atlantic became affordable and accessible to many. Establishing year-round cruising and highlighting the "pampering" experience of the ship while you sample exotic destinations was a brilliant move that launched today's cruise industry. This once-dying industry is now thriving.

Write two to four paragraphs that include:
- why you think this sector of the travel industry is doing so well.
- what percentage of the market it has gained (in other words, the number of people who have cruised).
- what the potential is for growth of the industry.
- what are some of the newest features and services being introduced and offered by the cruise industry (after doing some research).
- what your predictions are for the future of the cruise industry.

_____

_____

_____

_____

_____

_____

_____

_____

_____

_____

_____

_____

_____

_____

_____

_____

_____

_____

Name   Date

Directions: Define the following terms.

1. Adventure tour _____

_____

2. Affinity group _____

_____

3. Cancellation penalty _____

_____

4. Ecotour _____

_____

5. Escorted tour _____

_____

6. FIT _____

_____

7. Fly/drive _____

_____

8. Forced single _____

_____

9. Hard adventure _____

_____

10. Host _____

_____

11. Hosted tour _____

_____

12. Independent tour _____

_____

(continued)

13. Land rate _____

_____

14. NTA _____

_____

15. Package _____

_____

16. Pied Piper _____

_____

17. Single supplement _____

_____

18. Soft adventure _____

_____

19. Special-interest tour _____

_____

20. Step-on guide _____

_____

21. Template _____

_____

22. Tour _____

_____

23. Tour escort _____

_____

24. Tour guide _____

_____

25. Tour operator _____

_____

(continued)

Name   Date

26. Tour wholesaler _____

_____

27. USTOA _____

_____

Name   Date

Directions: Indicate which type of tour/package is described by each of the following statements.

Description		**Type of Tour**
1. Also known as an FIT	————————————	a. Independent tour
2. Although all tours are sometimes called "packages," this type is most often called by that name.	————————————	b. Hosted tour
		c. Escorted tour
3. Involves traveling with a group, limiting freedom of choice and action	————————————	d. Customized tour
4. A fly-drive, for example	————————————	
5. Most often chosen for a trip to Las Vegas	————————————	
6. Very often chosen for a trip to a Caribbean island	————————————	
7. Most likely choice for Americans traveling to China	————————————	
8. An African safari, a specialized version of this type of tour	————————————	

(continued)

Directions: For those destinations you are familiar with, indicate which special interest it might be associated with; then research the other destinations and indicate which special interests they might be associated with. Add the state or country in which the destination is located.

Special interest

a. Skiing   b. Diving   c. Tennis   d. Art   e. Music

f. Theater   g. Ancient history   h. Mountain climbing   i. Wildlife viewing   j. Religion

Destination

9. Sun Valley _____

10. Hilton Head _____

11. Santa Fe _____

12. Branson _____

13. Marathon Key _____

14. Athens _____

15. Lourdes _____

16. Masai Mara _____

17. London _____

18. The Matterhorn _____

Name   Date

Directions: Answer the following questions on Tauck Tour's "America's Canyonlands" by going to www.tauck.com, entering "Canyonlands" into the search box, and clicking on the brochure picture.

1. How long is the tour?

   8 days

2. View the full itinerary, and list the three canyons and national park that visitors will enjoy.

   grand canyon, bryce canyon, zion national

3. One of the largest man-made lakes in the world is part of the tour. What is it?

   lake Powell

4. Is Internet access available at all the hotels?

5. How many states will the tour cover, and what are they?

   Nevada, Utah, ~~Colorado~~ Arizona

6. In what city does the tour start, and where does it end?

   Starts Phoenix/Scottsdale
   ends Las Vegas

7. In what months is the tour offered?

   April - october

8. Do you need to be concerned with tipping?

   No, they are included

9. What type of weather will visitors encounter?

   Phoenix - May - Sep   hot and dry

(continued)

10. List the four additional excursions available.

_____

_____

_____

_____

11. What, if any, luggage restrictions are there on the motorcoach?

50 lbs   68 in → l×w×h

_____

12. When must a deposit be made, and when is final payment due?

$350 at time of booking
Final due 60 days before departure

13. Can a person be removed from the tour? Explain.

_____

_____

Name   Date

Directions: Provide the information requested.

1. Identify three features of tours that may benefit clients.

   a. _____

   b. _____

   c. _____

2. Identify three features of escorted tours, in particular, that may benefit clients.

   a. _____

   b. _____

   c. _____

3. Identify two drawbacks of escorted tours.

   a. _____

   b. _____

4. Describe three benefits that travel agencies derive from selling tours.

   a. _____

   b. _____

   c. _____

Directions: Circle the letter indicating the best answer.

5. What is most true about incentive tours?
   a. They are a good place to start for a travel counselor or associate of a tour company.
   b. Because they are free to the winners, accommodations and service need not be of the highest quality.
   c. They are generally combined with conventions and meetings.
   d. They should be meticulously planned and offer some special amenity or event.

6. The vast majority of tour prices listed in brochures are given
   a. per couple.
   b. per person double occupancy.
   c. per single person.
   d. per room.

(continued)

7. Full payment for tours is generally due
   a. 1 to 7 days before departure.
   b. 7 to 14 days before departure.
   c. 14 to 30 days before departure.
   d. 30 to 60 days before departure.

8. One good way of evaluating tour operators is to see if they are members of
   a. ASTA.
   b. WATA.
   c. USTOA.
   d. SITE.

Directions: Indicate whether following statements are true or false. If part or all of the statement is false, explain why.

9. The hallmark of a good escorted tour is that it changes hotels almost every night, enabling travelers to experience different things everyday. True or false?

   _____

   _____

10. A tour escort needs to be an expert in the area in which the tour is operating. True or false?

    _____

    _____

11. Those selling special-interest tours should become knowledgeable in that specialty before they start selling. True or false?

    _____

    _____

Name _____   Date _____

Directions: Search the Internet to complete the following exercises.

1. What is the motto of the United States Tour Operators Association?

   _____

   _____

2. Visit the Web site of the National Tour Association. Briefly describe their main mission.

   _____

   _____

   _____

   _____

3. Answer the following questions about Tauck Tours.

   a. Name at least four types of tours offered, and give a brief description.

   _____

   _____

   _____

   _____

   _____

   _____

   _____

   _____

   b. Briefly describe their World of Giving program.

   _____

   _____

   _____

   _____

(continued)

4. Find information about Gray Line's "Best of Sydney" Tour. (If the tour is no longer listed at Gray Line's Web site, select another basic tour of a large city of your choice.)

   a. How long is the tour?

   _____

   b. How much does it cost in Australian dollars? (How much is that in U.S. dollars?)

   _____

5. Write the title of one of the lead articles in this month's *Jax Fax Travel Marketing Magazine*. (Browse any of the other sections of its Web site that seem interesting.)

   _____

6. After examining the Web site of *Specialty Travel Index*, choose a specialty area of travel that you might enjoy selling now or in the future. What tour operators offer this specialty? Choose an operator that sounds most interesting to you, visit its Web site, and jot down information that increases your passion for this specialty.

   Specialty:

   _____

   Tour operators:

   _____

   _____

   _____

   _____

   Selected operator:

   _____

   _____

   _____

   _____

   _____

   _____

Name   Date

Directions: Consider the following concepts and issues. Conduct research to help you respond, and be prepared to discuss the topic in class.

Dynamic Packaging

According to the United States Tour Operator's Association (USTOA), today's travelers want to experience destinations more in-depth, including the local culture. However, Americans tend to take shorter trips than their European counterparts. Therefore, customized tours designed to match their interests and needs is very appealing to today's traveler. Tour operators and travel counselors are faced with the challenge of designing these tours to meet the needs of their customers and still make a profit. Some industry experts have proposed that technology can assist travel professionals with this challenge. "Dynamic Package" is using technology to assemble individual tour components and add a markup of the user's choosing, creating a custom-designed package with a single price in a matter of seconds.

Check several trade Web sites to learn the latest about dynamic packaging (pricing). Write two paragraphs regarding:
- What you learned about dynamic packaging
- How the industry views dynamic packaging
- What advantages and disadvantages you discovered
- Whether you think more industry professionals will use this new technology along with your reasons

Name _____   Date _____

Directions: Define the following terms.

1. Bait-and-switch _____

   _____

2. Cooperative advertising _____

   _____

3. CRM _____

   _____

4. Customer relationship marketing _____

   _____

5. Direct mail _____

   _____

6. Dual distribution _____

   _____

7. Four Ps _____

   _____

8. Legacy airlines _____

   _____

9. Marketing plan _____

   _____

10. Market research _____

    _____

11. Niche _____

    _____

12. Promotion_____

    _____

(continued)

13. Public relations _____

_____

14. Segmental analysis _____

_____

Name _____   Date _____

Directions: Choose the brand that you know the most about from the segments of the travel industry listed below. Explain how that brand markets itself in relation to each of the 4 Ps. In other words, describe its product, promotion techniques, the place where it makes its sales, and pricing strategy.

1. Hotels: Motel 6, Holiday Inn Express, Embassy Suites, or Ritz Carlton

   Brand selected _____

   a. Product _____

   b. Promotion _____

   c. Place _____

   d. Price _____

   e. Do any of these marketing decisions seem inconsistent? _____

2. Cruise lines: Carnival, Great American Steamboat Company, Windjammer cruises, or Silversea

   Brand selected _____

   a. Product _____

   b. Promotion _____

   c. Place _____

   d. Price _____

   e. Do any of these marketing decisions seem inconsistent? _____

3. Car rental: Hertz, Alamo, or Enterprise

   Brand selected _____

   a. Product _____

   b. Promotion _____

   c. Place _____

   d. Price _____

   e. Do any of these marketing decisions seem inconsistent? _____

(continued)

Directions: Within each set of parentheses in the following sentence, circle one of the choices.

Your tour company runs *(deluxe, moderate-first class, budget)* *(adventure trips, religious pilgrimages, escorted sightseeing tours)* to *(Asia, Africa, South America)*.

(For instance, if you picked the first choice in each series, your sentence would read "Your tour company runs *deluxe adventure trips* to *Asia*.") Now, using specific examples, explain how a shift in each of the following might change your marketing strategy for selling these tours.

4. Demographics _____

   _____

   _____

5. Laws _____

   _____

   _____

6. Political situation _____

   _____

   _____

7. Economics _____

   _____

   _____

Name   Date

Directions: The agency you are affiliated with has blocked off 20 cabins on Carnival's *Sensation* for a 5-day Caribbean cruise. Staff members have had trouble finding customers and have only 30 days left to sell. They have asked for your advice in deciding how to promote the cruise.

1. What age group would you target? Why?

   _____

2. What income group would you target? Why?

   _____

3. Choose three of the following promotional methods, and briefly describe how you could use each to promote the cruise: (a) direct mail, (b) print advertising, (c) radio and television advertising, (d) the Internet, (e) public relations, or (f) personal selling.

   a. _____

   _____

   b. _____

   _____

   c. _____

   _____

Directions: Using the list of promotional methods in question 3, indicate which method or methods you would use in each of the following situations. (Be prepared to explain why you chose it.)

4. A travel agency in northern Minneapolis wants to sell a broad range of products to the people on its side of the city.

   _____

   _____

5. A cruise line specializing in Alaskan cruises wants to be seen by the general public as being very concerned about its effect on the environment.

   _____

   _____

6. An incoming tour operator in New Orleans hopes to attract clients or groups all over the world to its "Authentic America" tours.

   _____

   _____

(continued)

7. A hotel finds that the next three weekends are very slow and wants to fill its rooms.

_____

_____

8. A new car rental chain wants to establish a foothold with companies in its region and is willing to offer them special incentives if their employees book its cars.

_____

_____

9. A travel agency wishes to sell a group tour to large church groups in its area.

_____

_____

10. An airline wants to announce its latest discount airfare, which will be available for the next two weeks.

_____

_____

11. A tour company wants to keep in touch with all travel counselors and clients who booked its tours in the past year.

_____

_____

12. Amtrak hopes to bolster its image so Congress will increase its funding for the next five years.

_____

_____

Name _____   Date _____

Directions: Answer the following questions.

1. What are five elements of the marketing process?

   a. _____

   b. _____

   c. _____

   d. _____

   e. _____

2. How does marketing differ from selling?

   _____

   _____

   _____

3. What are some reasons for a supplier to use dual distribution of its products?

   _____

   _____

   _____

4. How could a computerized database be helpful in the marketing process?

   _____

   _____

   _____

5. What is the difference between a product-oriented marketing strategy and a market-oriented strategy? Give an example of each.

   _____

   _____

   _____

(continued)

Directions: Indicate whether each of the following would produce an example of (a) primary data or (b) secondary data.

6. Talking to your clients after they return from a trip

   _____

7. Having your clients fill out a questionnaire after they return from a trip

   _____

8. Getting data from the U.S. Travel Association Web site

   _____

9. Doing telephone interviews with potential clients in your zip code

   _____

10. Studying a tour operator's report on the demographics of past clients

    _____

Name _____ Date _____

Directions: Go to the Web sites www.abercrombiekent.com and www.applevacations.com (or others suggested by your instructor). Analyze how each deals with the four Ps discussed in Chapter 9.

Web site a. _____

Web site b. _____

1. Product

    a. _____

    _____

    b. _____

    _____

2. Promotion

    a. _____

    _____

    b. _____

    _____

3. Place

    a. _____

    _____

    b. _____

    _____

4. Price

    a. _____

    _____

    b. _____

    _____

Name

Date

Directions: Consider the following concepts and issues. Conduct research to help you respond, and be prepared to discuss the topic in class.

Integrated Marketing

Marketing is no longer just for the "marketing department." Organizations of all sizes have realized that to compete in today's business world customer-focused marketing must be integrated into all their business processes from accounting to front-line interactions with the customers. Technology has provided tools (databases) that help professionals deliver personalized service.

In one to two paragraphs explain how front-line, entry-level travel professionals use the marketing concepts you learned in Chapter 9 in their everyday interactions with their customers.

_____

_____

_____

_____

_____

_____

_____

_____

_____

_____

_____

_____

_____

_____

_____

_____

_____

Name   Date

Directions: Define the following terms.

1. Body language _____

    _____

2. Close-ended question _____

    _____

3. Cross-selling _____

    _____

4. Feedback question _____

    _____

5. Open-ended question _____

    _____

6. Outside sales agent _____

    _____

7. Selling up _____

    _____

Name

Date

Directions: *Travel Career Development* breaks the sales process into eight basic steps. Number the following questions and statements in the order that they would most likely occur during the sales process. Please note that one of the sales steps is represented by two statements.

_____ So, should we book the Club Med or the Sandals resort for you?

_____ Did you have any specific place in mind for this winter's trip?

_____ Your documents should be in any day, and I will call you and deliver them as soon as they arrive.

_____ I've found two tours of Eastern Europe that would best match the general list of places you want to visit. Let me point out the highlights of each of them on this large map of the area.

_____ The *Sensation* offers both of the sports that you enjoy, and it visits the ports that you are most interested in.

_____ Ah, an excellent choice of hotel! Will that be check or credit card?

_____ Ah, a beautiful spot for scuba-diving; I snorkeled there once myself.

_____ Yes, it does tend to rain a lot, but that's what makes Ireland so lush and green all year.

_____ I see; so tickets to the Vienna Boys' Choir, the Spanish Riding School, and the Salzburg festival are absolutely essential for your trip to Austria this summer.

Name   Date

Directions: Describe a benefit that each of the following features might offer a client.

1. We can reserve and ticket any airline.

   _____

   _____

2. All our counselors have traveled extensively.

   _____

   _____

3. We deliver tickets.

   _____

   _____

4. The price of this tour is all-inclusive.

   _____

   _____

5. This tour has a step-on guide at each stop.

   _____

   _____

6. This tour includes round-trip transfers.

   _____

   _____

7. Your hotel is right on the beach.

   _____

   _____

8. Your hotel is in a remote location.

   _____

   _____

(continued)

9. All meals are included.

   _____

   _____

10. No meals are included.

   _____

   _____

Name _____   Date _____

Directions: Your clients, Mr. and Mrs. Safire, and their two children, ages 14 and 8, are planning a vacation to Disney World in Orlando, Florida. They are having a difficult time choosing a hotel. Write five questions that will enable you to discover their expectations and needs so that you can recommend a hotel. Label each question as open-ended, close-ended, or feedback. Make sure that you include at least one question from each category.

1. _____

   _____

2. _____

   _____

3. _____

   _____

4. _____

   _____

5. _____

   _____

Directions: Indicate whether each of the following recommendations is appropriate (A) or inappropriate (I). If it is inappropriate, rephrase it to make it appropriate.

6. I know you're going to love Disney World because all my clients do. A or I?

   _____

7. As you can see on the map, your hotel is right on the beach. A or I?

   _____

8. You have to eat at Babbo. It's the best restaurant in New York. A or I?

   _____

9. This tour meets all the requirements that you outlined. A or I?

   _____

10. The weather is always perfect in St. Thomas. A or I?

   _____

(continued)

Directions: The following attempts at closing a sale are so poor that they are more likely to lose the sale than to close it. Describe what is wrong with each and how you would change it.

11. Would you like to make a reservation today, or would you like to go home and think about it?

_____

_____

_____

_____

_____

12. Which of the seven brochures have you decided has the best package for you?

_____

_____

_____

_____

_____

13. That resort usually has rooms available at this time of year up to the last minute, so call me any time.

_____

_____

_____

_____

_____

14. Are you sure you want to book Tahiti? Fiji looks just as good, and Hawaii is even less expensive.

_____

_____

_____

_____

_____

Name   Date

Directions: Indicate whether the following statements are true or false. If part or all of the statement is false, explain why.

1. When a traveler has bought a vacation and has plane tickets and hotel vouchers in hand, he or she has purchased a tangible product. True or false?

   _____

2. Leisure travel, by its very nature, is discretionary. True or false?

   _____

3. A client who leans towards you with an open hand is exhibiting body language that indicates a readiness to buy. True or false?

   _____

4. When people cross their arms or legs, they are exhibiting body language that indicates that they accept what you are saying. True or false?

   _____

5. Benefits are more important than features. True or false?

   _____

Directions: Each of the following questions illustrates two types or categories of question. For each question, indicate the two types it illustrates, using the choices below. For example, "You wouldn't be thinking of buying this trip now, would you?" is an example of both a closing question and a close-ended question (but a very poor one).

Type

a. Qualifying   b. Open-ended   c. Close-ended   d. Closing   e. Feedback

Question

6. How many people will be in your party?   _____   _____

7. Would you like to take the cruise on the 21st or the 28th?   _____   _____

8. What would your dream trip look like if you could plan it any way you want?   _____   _____

9. Are you saying you want to see all five countries in the Alps on this trip?   _____   _____

10. What kinds of hotels do you usually stay in?   _____   _____

(continued)

Directions: Provide the information requested.

11. List five qualifying questions that are appropriate to ask if you are selling travel.

    a. _____

    b. _____

    c. _____

    d. _____

    e. _____

12. Describe two tools that you could use when presenting recommendations to clients.

    a. _____

    b. _____

13. Give two examples of how you could cross-sell to a client who called only to rent a car.

    a. _____

    b. _____

14. Describe how travel counselors can ensure customer satisfaction after a sale is made.

    _____

    _____

    _____

Name   Date

Directions: Table 10.1 on pages 254–5 in *Travel Career Development* lists motives for leisure travel and destinations that might appeal to travelers with those motives. Name one destination not listed in Table 10.1 that is likely to appeal to travelers with the following motives.

1. Gambling _____

2. Shopping _____

3. Religion _____

4. Sun _____

5. Food and drink _____

6. Entertainment _____

7. Arts _____

8. History and culture _____

9. Collecting countries _____

10. Meeting people _____

11. Personal challenge _____

12. Ecotourism _____

13. Sightseeing _____

14. Special events _____

15. Relaxation _____

16. Active sports _____

Directions: For practice using the Internet to expand your knowledge about selling techniques, complete the following exercises.

17. Enter the word "selling" in the Search box at *Travel Weekly*'s Web site, www.travelweekly.com. How many articles are listed that deal with the topic in some way?

_____

18. Search for an article on sales tips or techniques by entering terms such as "selling techniques," "sales tips," and "sales seminars" in the Search box at *Travel Weekly*'s Web site. Describe an idea about selling that is not included in your textbook.

_____

Name   Date

Directions: Consider the following concepts and issues. Conduct research to help you respond, and be prepared to discuss the topic in class.

Is It Service or Sales?

Salespeople are not selling products—they are fulfilling the needs of their customers. They can't fulfill those needs if they haven't discovered them. In the process of uncovering clients' needs and matching products and services to meet those needs, sales professionals build relationships with their customers. Clients feel served or serviced rather than sold. This distinction is critical to the long-term success of any sales professional. In your own words, write one to two paragraphs about how customer-focused sales (uncovering needs and building relationships) benefit (1) the seller, (2) the customer, and (3) the company or business.

_____

_____

_____

_____

_____

_____

_____

_____

_____

_____

_____

_____

_____

_____

_____

_____

_____

HPB-Ohio
3860 La Reunion Pkwy.
Dallas, TX 75212
serviceohio@hpb.com

Items :

Qty	Title	Locator
1	TRAVEL CAREER DEVELOPMENT-STUD	L01-2-10-013-001-213

Marketplace: AmazonMarketplaceUS
Order Number: 4172933
Ship Method: Standard
Customer Name: FHEG Accounts Payable
Order Date: 8/28/2019 7:37:07 AM
Marketplace Order #: 114-3317907-2430610
Email: wy0ny609r62npk7@marketplace.amazon.com

If you have any questions or concerns regarding this order, please contact us at serviceohio@hpb.com

Name _____   Date _____

Directions: Define the following terms.

1. ADA _____

_____

2. Baggage and personal possessions insurance _____

_____

3. CEIR _____

_____

4. CIC _____

_____

5. Commercial agency _____

_____

6. Ethnic agencies _____

_____

7. Flight insurance _____

_____

8. Honeymoon specialist _____

_____

9. Inbound travel _____

_____

10. Incentive house _____

_____

11. LGBT travel specialist _____

_____

12. Meeting _____

_____

(continued)

13. Meeting planner _____

_____

14. MPI _____

_____

15. SATH _____

_____

16. SITE _____

_____

17. Soft adventure _____

_____

18. Travel accident and health insurance _____

_____

19. Travelers with disabilities _____

_____

20. Trip cancellation or interruption insurance _____

_____

Name   Date

Directions: Indicate whether each statement is true or false. If a statement is false, explain why.

1. A bulkhead seat generally is a good choice for a person with a physical disability because of the extra legroom. True or false?

   _____

2. A seat in the emergency exit row is generally a good choice for a person with a physical disability because of the extra legroom. True or false?

   _____

3. Blind people are allowed to take their Seeing Eye dogs on flights. True or false?

   _____

4. All Amtrak coaches are equipped to transport passengers with disabilities. True or false?

   _____

5. Most long-distance motorcoach services in the United States have wheelchair lifts on the coach. True or false?

   _____

6. Most car rental companies can provide hand-controlled vehicles for renters with disabilities. True or false?

   _____

7. At least one bathroom aboard most of today's planes can accommodate passengers in wheelchairs. True or false?

   _____

8. Most cruise ships carry Seeing Eye dogs aboard at no extra cost. True or false?

   _____

9. Special provisions must be made to take a battery-operated wheelchair on a flight. True or false?

   _____

10. Passengers with disabilities can order food and drink at their seats on Amtrak. True or false?

    _____

Name _____   Date _____

Directions: Answer the following questions.

1. Mr. Fastow is afraid that if he becomes ill or has an accident before his trip, he may lose all or most of the money that he pays for the trip. How can you help him?

   _____

   _____

   _____

2. Mr. Skilling's mother is ill. He is afraid that if she takes a turn for the worse, he will have to cancel his trip and will lose all or most of the money he pays for the trip. Can you help him and, if so, how?

   _____

   _____

   _____

3. Ms. Watkins usually travels with very expensive clothing for presentations and award ceremonies. She is afraid that if the airline loses her luggage, her loss will far exceed the compensation from the airline. Can you lessen her fears?

   _____

   _____

   _____

4. The Lands are 72-year-olds and will be traveling overseas for the first time since they retired. They are concerned that Medicare doesn't cover them in other countries. Are their concerns valid, and can you ease them?

   _____

   _____

   _____

5. Shelly Mattura is a single mom who is starting her own business and flying a lot to meet people. She is concerned about flying and worried that if anything happens to her, her daughter will be left without enough funds for school. Can you ease her concerns?

   _____

   _____

   _____

(continued)

6. A group of trekkers are going to explore the source of the Zambezi River in Africa. They wonder what might happen to them in case of illness or accident while they are in the bush away from civilization. What can you do for them?

_____

_____

_____

7. Three years ago, when your client lived in another city, he booked a cruise with a line that went bankrupt before the date of the cruise. It took him two years to get some of his money back, and he didn't get much. He doesn't want to take the chance that this could happen again. How can you reassure him?

_____

_____

_____

Name _____   Date _____

Directions: Provide the following information.

1. Name two characteristics of business travel that make it an advantageous market for travel agencies.

   a. _____

   b. _____

2. List several key needs specific to business travelers.

   _____

   _____

   _____

   _____

3. Choose two of the following types of specialized groups, and briefly describe the special service they require: senior citizens, honeymooners, members of a religious group, or family travelers.

   a. _____

   _____

   b. _____

   _____

4. Name three things that a meeting planner might do that most travel counselors would not see as their function.

   a. _____

   b. _____

   c. _____

5. Comment on the following statement: "Because incentive trips are usually given free as rewards, they do not have to meet the high standards of trips that travelers pay for themselves."

   _____

   _____

   _____

   _____

(continued)

Directions: Heather Hardaway decided to sell group travel, but her first attempts were not very successful. Below are some the steps she took. What changes would you recommend in each step?

6. Because she loves skiing, Heather decided to sell ski trips to organizations in her area.

_____

_____

_____

7. She contacted the president of one social club and gave a presentation to her.

_____

_____

_____

8. She met with another organization at its monthly meeting and provided members with many destination choices, from Utah to Vermont. She even mentioned the most famous places in the Alps. She also made it clear that she was happy to book any week they chose.

_____

_____

_____

9. When Heather finally sold a trip to one small group, she booked all of the arrangements directly with hotels, transportation companies, and ski facilities. Participants later said they were dissatisfied with the location of the hotels relative to the ski lifts and with the fact that the transportation did not run to the resort when their plane was late.

_____

_____

_____

10. For the group that she booked, Heather made sure she received a 10 percent commission on all her arrangements. She figured that because she earns a 10 percent commission when she arranges travel for two people, making the same arrangements for 20 to 30 people at one time at that rate would give her a hefty profit.

_____

_____

_____

Name   Date

Directions: Use the Internet to answer the following questions.

1. In what specialty areas does ASTA offer home-study courses?

   _____

   _____

   _____

2. What ship that services the North American market has the most wheelchair-accessible cabins? What else does this ship offer passengers with a physical disability?

   _____

   _____

   _____

3. Where will the next World Congress of the Society for Accessible Travel and Hospitality be held?

   _____

4. What specialty trip described on www.specialtytravel.com would you like to take and love to sell to others?

   _____

5. Go to the Web site for *Meetings & Conventions Magazine*. Describe an insight or interesting fact that you learned, and be prepared to share it with your fellow students.

   _____

   _____

   _____

Name   Date

Directions: Consider the following concepts and issues. Conduct research to help you respond, and be prepared to discuss the topic in class.

Developing a Niche

Specializing in a specific area or niche has been the formula for success for many travel professionals. The niche they choose can be a type of travel, a specific segment of the market (type of traveler), or a destination. Whichever they choose, they create a distinctive identity and establish themselves as experts in meeting the special needs of this niche.

Explore the leading travel organizations' Web sites to learn more about developing a niche in the travel industry. Answer the following questions in one paragraph each:
- What factors should I consider when choosing a niche or specialization?
- What resources are available to help me develop my expertise in a niche?

_____

_____

_____

_____

_____

_____

_____

_____

_____

_____

_____

_____

_____

_____

_____

_____

_____

_____

_____

Name _____   Date _____

Directions: Define the following terms.

1. E-mail _____

_____

2. Fax _____

_____

3. Videoconferencing _____

_____

4. Voice mail _____

_____

5. Webcasting_____

_____

Name _____ Date _____

Directions: Answer the following questions.

1. What are three steps you can take to compensate for the ways that the telephone distorts the human voice?

   a. _____

   b. _____

   c. _____

2. What are three techniques that you can use when selling by telephone in order to help make up for the absence of body language?

   a. _____

   b. _____

   c. _____

Directions: Translate the following statements into language that a novice traveler can understand easily.

3. (By a travel counselor) My CRT shows that flight is a no-op on 7-12.

   _____

   _____

4. (By a member of the cruise staff) You'll have to tender in at that port.

   _____

   _____

Directions: In the following scenarios, a potential client calls a travel agency and a travel counselor responds. How would you improve the travel counselor's response to these callers in order to convert them to buyers?

5. "I saw an ad in the Sunday paper from ABC Travel for a $199 airfare from Los Angeles to Boston. Can you book it?"

   "I've never heard of that fare."

   _____

   _____

   _____

(continued)

6. "I just read an interesting article about Bermuda. I'll probably never go, but I'd like to know more. Do you have any information you could send me?"

   "Call the Bermuda Department of Tourism for general information, and then call us back if you ever decide to go."

   _____

   _____

   _____

7. "What can you tell me about tours to Alaska?"

   "There's too much information to explain on the telephone. You'll have to come in to the office."

   _____

   _____

   _____

8. "I'd like to speak to someone in your office who has been on a safari."

   "No one here has ever been. Sorry."

   _____

   _____

   _____

Name _____ Date _____

Directions: Circle the correctly spelled word in each of the following word groups.

1. accomodation   accommodation

2. itinerery   itinerary

3. luxury   luxery

4. computer   computor

5. commission   commision

6. cancelation   cancellation

7. insurance   insurence

8. occupancy   occupency

9. guarantee   guarentee

10. delux   deluxe

Directions: Indicate which of the following words is spelled correctly, and write the correct spelling for the incorrect ones.

11. separate   _____

12. occured   _____

13. Carribean   _____

14. Britian   _____

15. inoculation   _____

16. overide   _____

17. benefited   _____

18. accompanied   _____

19. reccommend   _____

20. Mediterrainean _____

Name   Date

Directions: Your agency has received the following letter or email:

> To Whom it May Concern:
>
> I am writing to express my concern about some things that happened to me on my recent trip to Denver, which I booked through your agency.
>
> I know I saved money by flying Air Apparent from here to Chicago and connecting with the big airline there, but I did not realize that I would have to carry my bags so much. They told me that I could not send my bags all the way through to Denver and as a result I had to carry them up two flights of stairs and a very long distance at the Chicago airport. This threw my back out and I had to spend the first two days at my sister-in-law's house lying on a couch. I distinctly remember that last year I was able to send my bags all the way through from here to Denver.
>
> When I came back from Denver, I missed my flight because the lady told me I had not arrived in time. That was a lie. I was at the airport waiting for an hour and then was in the bathroom when they told us to get on the plane so I did not hear the announcement. You told me that if I had my boarding ticket, I could get right on the plane, but the lady at the gate said that someone else had my seat!
>
> I had to wait for the next flight and my brother, who flies all the time, says I should have gotten at least $300 in compensation.
>
> I am very angry about this and feel that I should be compensated.
>
> Yours sincerely,

Write a reply to explain what happened. Consider the following:
- How could the baggage problem have occurred?
- How could the boarding confusion have occurred?
- What are the rules regarding denied boarding compensation?

_____

_____

_____

_____

_____

_____

_____

_____

(continued)

Name _____ Date _____

Directions: Answer the following questions.

1. When is a letter likely to be your best form of communication?

   _____

   _____

2. What are four elements that a procedure or policy manual should contain?

   a. _____

   b. _____

   c. _____

   d. _____

3. What are five guidelines for using e-mail effectively?

   a. _____

   b. _____

   c. _____

   d. _____

   e. _____

Directions: For each of the following situations, indicate which method of communication is likely to be most effective: (a) face-to-face, (b) written letter, (c) fax, (d) phone call, or (e) e-mail.

4. Your airline just received a letter of complaint from a traveler, and you need to clarify what happened before you can act.

   _____

5. Documents have been received at your travel agency, and you want to inform the client that they are being sent out today.

   _____

6. Your hotel has just received a request for 15 rooms a month from now from a small tour company. You want to inform the booking agent at the tour company about payment deadlines, cancellation penalties, and other stipulations concerning the reservation.

   _____

(continued)

7. A client whose business travel you have booked for the past three months wants to take a trip to Europe with her family next year and asks for information.

   _____

8. A client who took one of your tour packages contacted his travel counselor who, in turn, has contacted you and described in detail the promised amenities that he did not receive. They request a partial refund A.S.A.P.

   _____

9. Your boss has decided on a major new sales campaign and wants you to contact the high-volume travel agencies in your area to explain it to them.

   _____

10. You need to inform a colleague about a meeting scheduled next week, but you know he's out of the office today.

   _____

11. A client is going to Turkmenistan in two months, and you want to tell her about passport and visa regulations, State Department warnings and suggestions, and available insurance.

   _____

12. You want your client to go over the detailed itinerary that you have prepared for his four-week journey to China.

   _____

13. A client's reservation is about to be canceled because she has not paid her deposit.

   _____

Name   Date

Directions: For additional practice using the Internet, complete the following exercises.

1. Look up the word *infrastructure* at www.dictionary.com, and list items in the definition that relate to tourism.

   _____

   _____

   _____

2. Find one tip online about e-mail that was not included in the textbook.

   _____

   _____

   _____

3. How much does it cost to send a one-ounce airmail letter to London via the U.S. mail? Go to the postal service at www.usps.com; click first on "Calculate Postage" and then on "Calculate International Postage."

   _____

Name   Date

Directions: Consider the following concepts and issues. Conduct research to help you respond, and be prepared to discuss the topic in class.

Webinars

You are a corporate travel counselor who specializes in meeting planning. One of your clients has asked you to join a webinar scheduled for next Tuesday with the managers of six branch offices to discuss the upcoming conference that you have been planning. Your client has set up a password for you to join online. Your computer has the necessary system requirements, software, and video camera. Would you communicate differently during the webinar than you would in a face-to-face meeting?

List any special considerations you would make to ensure that you communicate effectively during the webinar. (Hint: Include both audio and visual considerations).

_____

_____

_____

_____

_____

_____

_____

_____

_____

_____

_____

_____

_____

_____

_____

_____

_____

_____

Name _____   Date _____

Directions: Define the following terms.

1. Accountable document _____

   _____

2. ARC report _____

   _____

3. Area Bank Settlement Plan _____

   _____

4. Base fare _____

   _____

5. Cash flow _____

   _____

6. Consortium _____

   _____

7. Escrow account _____

   _____

8. Income statement _____

   _____

9. Invoice _____

   _____

10. MCO _____

    _____

11. PTA _____

    _____

12. Receipt _____

    _____

13. Rent-a-desk _____

    _____

(continued)

14. Voucher _____

_____

Name   Date

Directions: State whether each of the following is a (a) fixed expense, (b) variable expense, or (c) semivariable (mixed) expense.

1. Rent _____ Fixed

2. Advertising _____ Semivariable

3. Commissions to outside salespersons and bonuses to employees _____ Variable

4. Salaries _____ fixed

5. Telephone service _____ Semivariable

6. Insurance _____ fixed

Directions: On a particular day you made the following bookings. Assume a 10 percent commission on all components unless stated otherwise; do not include port charges or any taxes in your calculations. What commission will you earn for each booking?

7. Hyatt Regency Aruba Resort & Casino for two people in a double for two nights at a rate of $235 per night.

    $235 + 235 = 470$ $470 \times .10 = 47$

8. Hyatt Regency Aruba Resort & Casino for two people, each in a single room, for two nights, at a rate of $205 per night.

    $205 + 205 = 410$
    $205 + 205 = 410$ $410 \times .10 = 41$ $820 \times .10 = 82$
    820

9. A Hertz car rental at the rate of $199 weekly and $39 per extra day. The car is picked up on June 1 at 9 A.M. and returned on June 11 at 5 P.M.

    39
    $\times 4$
    June 7 $199 + 156 = 355$ 35.50

10. A party of four adults whose airline tickets come to $3,200 (base fare) with a 7 percent commission rate and a $50 commission cap.

    $3200 / 4 = 800 \times .07 = 56$ 50 per ticket 200 total

11. A party of four adults whose airline tickets come to $1,200 (base fare) with a 7 percent commission rate and a $50 commission cap.

    $1,200 / 4 = 300 \times .07 = 21$ 21 per ticket 84 total

12. A client takes Amtrak from Washington to New York for $199 round trip. He rents a car for three days at $49 per day and stays at a hotel for three nights at $189 per night. What is the total commission you earned for his trip?

    $199 + (49 \times 3) + (189 \times 3) = 913 \times .10 = 91.30$
    $199 + 147 + 567$

(continued)

13. You have sold a deluxe tour to two clients for $6,000 total; the commission is 10 percent. A comprehensive insurance policy including trip cancellation/ interruption, medical/accident coverage, and baggage insurance will cost them $150 per person. The insurance company pays you 30 percent commission. What will be the dollar amount of your commission on the entire trip, including the insurance?

$$6,150 \times 2 \quad 6,000 \times 2 = 12,000 \quad 150 \times 150 = 300 \times .30 = 90$$
$$\times .10 = 600 \quad 600 + 90 = 690 \; total$$

14. The cruise you have sold costs $1,299 per person, double occupancy, commissionable at 10 percent. Each of your two clients already has paid you a $200-per-person deposit.

   a. When final payment is due, how much must you collect?

   $$1,299 \times 2 = 2598 - 400 = 2,198$$

   b. What is your total commission?

   $$2598 \times .10 = 259.80 \qquad 2198 \times .10 = 219.80$$

   c. How much will you now send to the cruise line for final payment after deducting your commission?

   $$2598 - 259.80 = 2338.20 \quad 2378.20$$
   $$219.80$$

15. When you sell $20,000 worth of tours with A-B-C Tours, you receive a 2 percent override above your 10 percent commission.

   a. How much is the override?

   $$20000 \times .02 = \boxed{400} \quad 20000 \times .10 = 2000 + 400 = 2400$$

   b. The override represents what percent increase in your commission?

Name   Date

Directions: Answer the following questions.

1. A travel agency is owed $650 in hotel commissions and $4,000 from a group for a deposit that you have forwarded to hold space on a cruise. Is the $4,650 listed on your balance sheet under assets or liabilities?

   asset ——> money coming in

2. Is the amount of equity or the amount of stock held by the owners of a company listed on the balance sheet as an asset or a liability?

   asset

3. Is the financial position of a business at a particular time found on the income statement or the balance sheet?

   income statement

4. Is a summary of revenue and expenses over three months done on the income statement or the balance sheet?

   income statement

5. Besides wanting to avoid the need to pay immediately or to carry large amounts of cash, what is another major reason that clients may wish to pay by credit card in other countries?

   exchange rate

Directions: Indicate whether each statement is true or false. If the statement is false, explain why.

6. You can accept a credit card from a stranger over the phone as long as you receive an approval code through your computer or via phone. True or false?

   false

7. You can accept a personal check from a stranger as long as he or she shows you a picture ID and signs the check in front of you. True or false?

   false

8. You can accept traveler's checks from a stranger as long as he or she shows you a passport or other ID that matches his or her name and signature. True or false?

   true

9. You can accept cash from a stranger as long as it's not counterfeit. True or false?

   true

10. Most agencies prefer to accept a credit card from a stranger rather than a check. True or false?

    true

Name   Date

Directions: Visit *Travel Weekly*'s Web site, and answer the following questions.

1. Enter "overrides" in its search box. Choose one article and summarize it in a few sentences.

_____

_____

_____

_____

_____

_____

_____

2. Enter "credit card fraud" in its search box. Choose one article and summarize it in a few sentences.

_____

_____

_____

_____

_____

_____

_____

Name   Date

_____

Directions: Consider the following concepts and issues. Conduct research to help you respond, and be prepared to discuss the topic in class.

Travel Agency Profitability

The methods in which travel agencies make money have shifted. Some agencies didn't adapt to the changes in the industry well and closed their doors. Others have found creative ways to provide new services to their clients and are adopting sound business practices that allow them to make healthy profits.

What actions and strategies can travel agencies take to become and remain profitable? Write two paragraphs that include strategies along with an explanation as to why you believe these strategies can be successful.

_____

_____

_____

_____

_____

_____

_____

_____

_____

_____

_____

_____

_____

_____

_____

_____

_____

_____

_____

Name _____   Date _____

Directions: Define the following terms.

1. Business plan _____

   _____

2. Cloud _____

   _____

3. Errors and omissions and general liability insurance _____

   _____

4. Independent contractor _____

   _____

5. NACTA _____

   _____

6. OSSN _____

   _____

7. Social media _____

   _____

8. Telecommute _____

   _____

9. VTC _____

   _____

Name   Date

Directions: Answer the following questions.

1. In a sentence or two, list and describe five key ways in which an attorney's advice is necessary when setting up your home-based business.

   An attorney help you obtain licenses, contracts, insurance, and the type of business you will be. They can help you with your tax ID information and laws you will need to abide by.

2. In a sentence or two, list and describe five key pieces of office equipment that you are likely to need when setting up your home-based business.

   Computer, phone, desk, file cabinets, stationary, wifi, voicemail, email, cloud/googledocs, printer/scanner/fax

Name   Date

Directions: Provide the information requested.

1. List three factors that have contributed to the increasing numbers of home-based travel agencies.

   a. Advances in techonolgy —stay in touch with the central office

   b. hassles w/ commuting

   c. flexibility

   profitable + less expensive

2. List the criteria that must be met for the IRS to consider a home-based agent an independent contractor.

   a. pay for their own supplies

   b. not employee / no control over your hours

   c. not elidgible for benefits

   d. not included in training

   e. no taxes taken out

   f. _____

3. A business plan includes the following three components:

   a. expectations + goals
   your name

   b. mission statement + purpose
   projections for the businur

   c. objectives

(continued)

4. Describe one advantage and one disadvantage of creating a home-based office to sell travel.

   a. Advantage

   Flexibility,

   a. Disadvantage

   distractions, develop clientel, self-providing

5. Once an agency's Web site is up and running, what additional tasks need to be done on a regular basis?

   a. updates it

   b. analytics

   c. marketing

Directions: Circle the letter indicating the best answer.

6. When selecting a host agency, independent contractors should consider
   a. if the host agency's specialization fits well with the independent contractor's niche.
   b. the agency's experience working with independent contractors.
   c. the level of support the independent contractor needs compared to the level of support the host agency will give.
   d. all of the above.

7. Home-based agents can develop their networks by
   a. establishing relationships with suppliers that specialize in the same niche.
   b. joining trade organizations.
   c. attending seminars, workshops, and trade shows.
   d. all of the above.

8. A pseudo identification number
   a. is recognized by a single supplier.
   b. is recognized by U.S. travel suppliers only.
   c. is recognized by the majority of travel suppliers worldwide.
   d. may be required by the state.

9. Customer relationship management is a business strategy that combines
   a. upgrades and selling-up.
   b. personalized service and technology
   c. cross-selling and technology.
   d. marketing and finance.

10. An employee of an agency who works out of his or her home is a(n)
    a. independent contractor.
    b. flex-employee.
    c. telecommuter.
    d. host agent.

(continued)

Name   Date

Directions: Search the Web in order to complete the following exercises.

1. Browse the contents of the "Home-Based Travel Agent Resource Center" at www.homebasedtravelagent.com. Answer the following questions.

   a. What scams does the author warn the reader to be cautious about?

   discount or free travel, Reward program, outrageous claims, → for recruiting others appeal to greed

   b. Choose another item of interest on the site, and describe it in a sentence or two.

   _____

   _____

   _____

   _____

2. Go to www.hometravelagency.com and find the article "Home-Based Agent Qualities That Lead to Success." List the qualities below.

   a. work w/ successful independent agents
   b. no unresolved formal complaints
   c. develop a professional independent agents network
   d. no "travel agent recruiting" program
   e. do not "travel agent ID cards"
   f. meaningful commissions + overrides,

3. List three benefits of joining NACTA.

   a. _____

   b. _____

   c. _____

4. List three benefits of joining OSSN.

   _____

   _____

   _____

   _____

Name   Date

Directions: Consider the following concepts and issues. Conduct research to help you respond, and be prepared to discuss the topic in class.

Mission Statements

Creating a mission statement is one of the first tasks you should perform during the planning stages of your new business. A mission statement defines the purpose of your business. Your mission statement should be a clear, concise statement that says what your agency is, what it does, for whom, and where. In just one or two sentences, a mission statement needs to communicate the unique essence of your company.

1. Conduct research on the Internet on how to write a mission statement.

2. Visit a number of travel agency Web sites, and read each of their mission statements. List three mission statements you feel are well-written.

    a. Company _____

       Mission   _____

                 _____

    b. Company _____

       Mission   _____

                 _____

    c. Company _____

       Mission   _____

                 _____

3. Write a mission statement for a home-based travel agency (specialty of your choice).

   _____

   _____

   _____

   _____

Name _____   Date _____

Directions: Define the following terms.

1. Application letter _____

   _____

2. Call center _____

   _____

3. CHRIE _____

   _____

4. Cover letter _____

   _____

5. Networking _____

   _____

6. Résumé _____

   _____

Name _____ Date _____

Directions: Conduct a self-assessment. For each of the following categories, list your qualifications and qualities.

1. Skills _____

    _____

    _____

2. Destination knowledge_____

    _____

    _____

3. Talents _____

    _____

    _____

4. Interests _____

    _____

    _____

5. Personal preferences _____

    _____

    _____

6. Accomplishments_____

    _____

    _____

7. Personal _____

    _____

    _____

Directions: Choose a position in the travel industry that interests you. (You might want to look again at Table 1.1 on page 16 in the textbook.) Now assume that you have been scheduled for an interview for that position. How would you answer the following questions during the interview?

8. What is it about this position that interests you?

    _____

(continued)

9. What do you see yourself doing five years from now?

_____

10. Tell me about two achievements of which you are most proud.

_____

_____

11. Give an example of a major problem you faced and how you solved it.

_____

_____

12. What is your greatest accomplishment?

_____

_____

13. Of all your jobs, which did you like best? Why?

_____

_____

14. Which job did you like least? Why?

_____

_____

15. If you could have made two improvements in your last job, what would they have been?

_____

_____

16. Why should you be my first choice for this position?

_____

_____

17. What five words best describe you?

_____

_____

Name _____   Date _____

Directions: Fill in this worksheet to use as a reference for your résumé.

Name _____

Address _____

Telephone (home) _____

Telephone (business) _____

Fax _____

E-mail _____

Career objective _____

Education (List the most
recent school first.) _____

Dates attended: From _____ to _____

Degree or diploma earned _____

Major and Minor subjects _____

Awards, honors, certificates _____

(Repeat the preceding section for each school attended after high school.)

High School _____

Dates attended: From _____ to _____

Diploma earned Yes _____ No _____

Work Experience (List the most recent job first.)

Name of firm _____

Address _____

Dates of employment: From _____ to _____

Title _____

Duties _____

Special achievements
(awards, citations,
commendations,
promotions, etc.) _____

(continued)

(Repeat the preceding section for each position held.)

Military experience _____

Related outside interests _____

_____

_____

Travels _____

_____

_____

References (on separate sheet) _____

_____

_____

1. On separate paper, write your résumé using the information from this worksheet.

2. On separate paper, write a cover letter that would be appropriate to apply for the position you selected.

Name _____   Date _____

Directions: Answer the following questions.

1. What are the distinguishing characteristics of the following types of travel positions?

   a. Nonpersonal phone work _____

   _____

   b. Personal intermediary of services _____

   _____

   c. In-person supplier of services _____

   _____

2. What are four key items that employers look for on an application or résumé?

   a. _____

   b. _____

   c. _____

   d. _____

3. What are three things you should do to prepare for an interview?

   a. _____

   b. _____

   c. _____

4. What are five sources of information about employment opportunities?

   a. _____

   b. _____

   c. _____

   d. _____

   e. _____

(continued)

Directions: Indicate whether each of the following statements is true or false. If a statement is false, explain why.

5. You should listen carefully for an opportunity to ask for a job during an information interview. True or false?

_____

6. You should always accompany a résumé with a cover letter. True or false?

_____

7. If you are offered two jobs, always take the one with the higher salary when you are starting without experience. True or false?

_____

8. Positions for travel counselors are found in every area of the country. True or false?

_____

9. Positions for airline reservationists are found in every area of the country. True or false?

_____

10. When you have an interview, find out how people dress in that office and dress accordingly. True or false?

_____

11. You should be a half-hour early for an interview to make sure you are on time. True or false?

_____

Worksheet 15.5 Technology Technique

Name   Date

Directions: Practice using the Internet to help in a job search by completing the following exercises.

1. Go to Hilton Hotels (www.hilton.com) and click on the "Careers" link at the bottom of the page. List three departments where undergraduate and graduate students can work as summer interns.

_____

_____

_____

2. Go to the Careers section of American Airlines' Web site (www.aa.com), and list at least one job currently available.

_____

_____

3. Look for employment opportunities listed at the Web site of Enterprise Corporation (www.enterprise.com). Note an entry-level position at a location near you.

_____

_____

4. Go to the job listing site, Monster (www.monster.com). Enter "hospitality tourism" in the search box plus your location. Note one job that you might want in the future. (Most job listings are for people with experience.)

_____

_____

5. Go to www.monster.com and examine the tips on résumés, interviews, and other job-finding skills. List one tip that you would like to share with other students.

_____

_____

6. Go to www.hottraveljobs.com. List two jobs that you might want in the future.

_____

_____

_____

Name   Date

Directions: Consider the following concepts and issues. First fill in the weaknesses, and then list the corresponding strengths.

Weaknesses = Overextensions of Strengths

The dreaded interview question almost always comes, "What are your weaknesses?" You know that you can't say, "I have no weaknesses," but which of your weaknesses won't seem so negative? Human nature is such that it is much easier for us to identify our weaknesses than it is for us to define our strengths.

It has been said, "Our weaknesses are merely overextensions of our strengths."
Do you agree with that philosophy? Try it for yourself by completing the following exercise.

Weakness
example:
Stubborn

Strength
example:
Determined, sees projects through to completion

Name _____   Date _____

Directions: Define the following terms.

1. Back-to-back ticketing _____

_____

2. Business development manager _____

_____

3. Card mills _____

_____

4. Corporate culture _____

_____

5. Doublebooking _____

_____

6. Hidden-city ticketing _____

_____

7. Mentor _____

_____

8. Professional _____

_____

Designations and Certifications

Directions: Define the following terms.

1. ACC _____

_____

2. CAS _____

_____

3. CITE _____

_____

4. CMP _____

_____

(continued)

5. CTA _____

_____

6. CTC _____

_____

7. CTIE _____

_____

8. CTP _____

_____

9. Destination Specialist _____

_____

10. DMC _____

_____

11. MCC _____

_____

12. TAP Test _____

_____

Name

Date

Directions: Read the following hypothetical situations, and choose the response that best reflects your judgment of what is ethical.

1. One of the car rental companies that you frequently recommend is giving laptop computers to travel agents who book 50 clients in one month. You need only one more booking to win, and it's the last day of the month. Just in time, a corporate traveler calls. When you suggest the car rental company that is offering the laptop, he says that he would prefer another company.

   What do you do? Circle a, b, or c.

   a. Tell the client that your agency has had favorable dealings with the company in question, that you recommend it highly, and then let him decide.

   b. Explain why that company is his only option and book him anyway.

   c. Book the client with the company of his preference and hope that someone else will call so you can win the laptop.

   What were the reasons and ethical principles that guided your selection?

   _____

   _____

   _____

   _____

2. After you have spent three hours researching and booking a high-commission European vacation, your client calls to say that she wants you to transfer this reservation to another agency. When you ask her why, she says that she likes it better and that it is located closer to her home. You know that you reserved the last two seats on her departing flight, and if you don't release her seats to the other agency, she probably won't be able to rebook.

   What do you do? Circle a, b, or c.

   a. Refuse to release, telling her it's against company policy (whether your agency has such a rule or not).

   b. Tell her you'll release. But cancel all her bookings after you hang up.

   c. Release the reservation.

   What were the reasons and ethical principles that guided your selection?

   _____

   _____

   _____

   _____

(continued)

3. Your best friend has always dreamed of taking a Caribbean cruise. She knows about familiarization (fam) trips and how cheaply you can sometimes travel on them. Please, she asks, can you book her on one of those trips? All it will take is a request on travel agency letterhead saying that she is an employee. She's a longtime friend who has done special favors for you in the past.

   What do you do? Circle a, b, or c.

   a. Book her on an upcoming cruise as long as she promises not to tell anybody that she's not really a travel agent.

   b. Tell her you're sorry, but you could lose your job if you got caught.

   c. Offer to find her an economical cruise she can afford instead of a fam trip.

   What were the reasons and ethical principles that guided your selection?

   _____

   _____

   _____

   _____

4. You've been offered a better salary and an opportunity for rapid advancement at a new agency. You accept. But alone in the office one evening, before you've given notice to your current employer, you realize that it would be easy to copy your agency's client list from your computer without anyone finding out. The list would help show your new boss that you know how to generate business.

   What do you do? Circle a, b, or c.

   a. Copy the list.

   b. Copy only the names of the clients you know are coming with you anyway.

   c. Decide not to copy anything, even though you're not particularly fond of your current boss.

   What were the reasons and ethical principles that guided your selection?

   _____

   _____

   _____

   _____

Name _____

Date

Directions: For each of the following skills, list a position within the travel and tourism industry in which that skill would be useful, and describe how the skill could be applied to that position. (Describing a situation or explaining how the skill could be used will be especially helpful.)

1. Organizational skills

   a. Position _____

   b. How can this skill be applied to the position you chose?

   _____

2. Time management skills

   a. Position _____

   b. How can this skill be applied to the position you chose?

   _____

3. Negotiating skills

   a. Position _____

   b. How can this skill be applied to the position you chose?

   _____

4. Understanding consumer trends and customer motivations

   a. Position _____

   b. How can this skill be applied to the position you chose?

   _____

5. Crisis management skills

   a. Position _____

   b. How can this skill be applied to the position you chose?

   _____

6. Business communication skills

   a. Position _____

   b. How can this skill be applied to the position you chose?

   _____

(continued)

7. Cultural diversity skills

    a. Position _____

    b. How can this skill be applied to the position you chose?

    _____

_____   Date
Name

Directions: Indicate whether each of the following statements is true or false. If it is false, explain why.

1. A good way to be successful on your new job is to do only what you are told so you don't get into trouble taking the initiative on tasks you have not yet learned. True or false?

   _____

2. A good way to be successful on your new job is to act as if you know the answers to most questions (especially with clients) even if you don't. True or false?

   _____

3. A good way to be successful on your new job is to find a person in the company whom you can emulate. True or false?

   _____

4. A good way to be successful on your new job is to help colleagues when necessary but avoid doing too much so that you aren't taken advantage of. True or false?

   _____

5. A good way to be successful on your new job is to tread softly in suggesting that changes be made until you have been with the company for awhile. True or false?

   _____

6. Following the corporate culture means obeying each rule and policy of the office to the letter. True or false?

   _____

Directions: Provide the information requested in the following exercises.

7. Describe five steps to move up the career ladder.

   a. _____

   b. _____

   c. _____

   d. _____

   e. _____

(continued)

8. List seven skills that are important for travel professionals to develop.

   a. _____

   b. _____

   c. _____

   d. _____

   e. _____

   f. _____

   g. _____

9. Describe how successful professionals approach change and why it is important to have a strategy to manage change in the travel industry.

   _____

   _____

   _____

10. Describe the ethical principle of confidentiality.

    _____

    _____

11. List three logical steps you might take to develop a specialization.

    a. _____

    b. _____

    c. _____

12. If you worked in a travel agency and were given the opportunity to specialize, what field would you choose? Describe two ways that you could promote your specialty to potential customers.

    _____

    _____

    _____

    _____

    _____

Name   Date

Directions: Complete the following exercises for practice using the Web to find information to help you build your career.

1. Go to www.thetravelinstitute.com, and find information about the TAP test.

   a. Is the TAP Test available online?

   _____

   b. What are three advantages or benefits of taking and passing the TAP Test?

   _____

   _____

   _____

2. Go to ASTA's Web site and click on the "Education & Careers" section. List one of the seminars, events, or specialty courses that would help you to advance your career.

   _____

   _____

3. Look at the fam trips offered at www.ossn.com. List one that you might enjoy or that might enhance your career.

   _____

   _____

4. Search Google for the phrase "11 Minimum Guidelines for Going Green." On what organization's Web site is the information found? List three of the guidelines that most appeal to you.

   _____

   _____

   _____

   _____

   _____

5. Go to CLIA's Web site (www.cruising.org), and list a seminar or course that might enhance your career. (You may have to search a bit to find CLIA's course offerings. Try clicking on "Agencies & Agents.")

   _____

   _____

(continued)

6. Go to the Association of Destination Management Executive's Web site. Describe its mission and list three ways it plans to reach this goal.

   Mission _____

   Methods used to reach its mission

   a. _____

   b. _____

   c. _____

7. Go to NTA's Web site, and enter "Travel Scams" in the search box. List three tips on this checklist.

   a. _____

   b. _____

   c. _____

8. Go to the Web site for CHRIE. What is its mission?

   _____

9. Go to SITE's Web site. When is their next convention and where will it be held?

   _____

10. Go to the Web site of the Convention Industry Council (www.conventionindustry.org). What is a CMP, and what are the requirements for certification as a CMP?

    _____

    _____

Name

Date

Directions: Consider the following concepts and issues. Conduct research to help you respond, and be prepared to discuss the topic in class.

Global Code of Ethics for Tourism

The Global Code of Ethics for Tourism is a comprehensive set of principles whose purpose is to guide the stakeholders in tourism development: central and local governments, local communities, the tourism industry and its professionals, as well as international and domestic visitors.

Find the set of principles along with their corresponding articles (on the WTO's Web site).

Choose one of the ten articles; explain its purpose and what actions are required by the stakeholders named above to adhere to the principle. Write a one-page report on your findings, and be prepared to discuss the topic in class.

Article # _____

Article statement _____

Purpose of Principle _____

_____

Explain the actions that can be taken by each responsible party (stakeholders in tourism development, governments, host communities, travel professionals, and/or tourists) to adhere to this principle.

_____

_____

_____

_____

_____

_____

_____

_____

_____

_____

_____

_____